Name _____

W9-AAU-478

## ▶ Directions

Say the name of each picture. Write its beginning letter on the lines, first as a capital letter and then as a small letter.

1.
_____

2.
_____

3.
_____

4.
_____

5.
_____

6.
_____

7.
_____

8.
_____

9.
_____

10.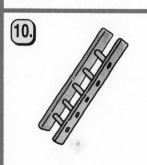
_____

11.
_____

12.
_____

13.
_____

14.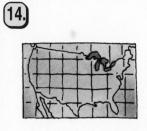
_____

15.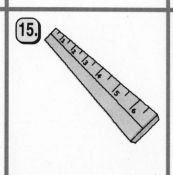
_____

16.
_____

© MCP All Rights Reserved.

Circle each word that begins with **q, s, v, w, y,** or **z.**

1. The Quinns were excited about their summer vacation.
2. They were going to Washington DC, for seven days.
3. Susan wanted to visit the home of the President.
4. Zack couldn't wait to see their cousins Vincent and Sally.
5. Mom said they would all climb the Washington Monument.
6. Dad was sure they would like to sail on the river.
7. All of the family wanted to visit the zoo.
8. Zack said the zebra was his very favorite animal.
9. His sister wanted to see a wolf with its yellow eyes.
10. Soon it was time for the Quinns to go.

**Directions**

Choose two of the sentences above.  Write the number of each sentence in the left-hand corner of each box.  Then draw a picture for each sentence.

Name  _____

© MCP All Rights Reserved.

> **Directions**
>
> Say the name of each picture. Write the consonant that stands for the sound you hear in the middle of each word.

| | | | |
|---|---|---|---|
| 1. 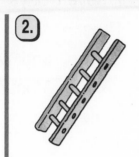 | 2.  | 3.  | 4. 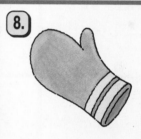 |
| 5.  | 6.  | 7.  | 8.  |
| 9.  | 10.  | 11.  | 12.  |
| 13.  | 14.  | 15. 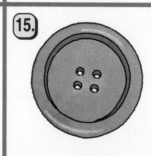 | 16.  |

Lesson 2: Medial consonants

3

Look at the picture. Read the sentence. Circle the word that will finish the sentence. Write the word on the line.

**1.** Mom took my _____ sister and me to the zoo.

baby          bunny

**2.** The zoo is by a park in our _____ .

cousin          city

**3.** First we saw a _____ at the zoo.

tiger          tulip

**4.** Then we came to the pond where the _____ lives.

honey          beaver

**5.** Next we saw a big cat called a _____ .
It had lots of spots!

leopard          lemon

**6.** After that we saw a _____ beside a cactus.

lizard          peanut

**7.** I got to ride on a _____ .

parrot          camel

**8.** As we left, she was _____ good-bye.

waving          wagon

Name _____

Look at the letter in each row. Then say the name of each picture. Color the pictures whose names end with the sound of that consonant.

1.

t

2.

k

3.

p

  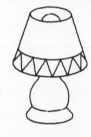 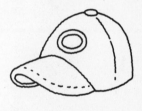

4.

x

   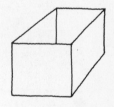

5.

l

© MCP All Rights Reserved.

Look at the picture. Fill in the circle beside the word that will finish the sentence. Write the word on the line.

1. Ben rides the _____ to school.
   - ○ bug
   - ○ bud
   - ○ bus

2. He likes to wear his red _____ .
   - ○ cat
   - ○ cap
   - ○ car

3. Ben takes his lunch in a _____ .
   - ○ bat
   - ○ bad
   - ○ bag

4. Today he has a _____ sandwich.
   - ○ ham
   - ○ hat
   - ○ had

5. Ben writes with his new _____ .
   - ○ pet
   - ○ pen
   - ○ peg

6. He will draw a _____ with it.
   - ○ map
   - ○ man
   - ○ mat

7. After school, Ben plays with his _____ .
   - ○ car
   - ○ cat
   - ○ cap

8. At eight o'clock he goes to _____ .
   - ○ beg
   - ○ bet
   - ○ bed

Name _____

▶ **Directions**

Write the consonant you hear **at the beginning** of each picture name.

1.

_____

2.

_____

3.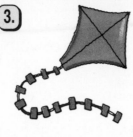

_____

4.

_____

▶ **Directions**

Write the consonant you hear **at the end** of each picture name.

5.

_____

6.

_____

7.

_____

8.

_____

▶ **Directions**

Write the consonants you hear **at the beginning** and **at the end** of each picture name.

9.

_____

10.

_____

11.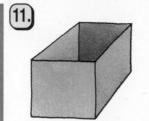

_____

12.

_____

© MCP All Rights Reserved.

Read the words in the box. Look at the letters below. Write each word from the box in the columns that describe the position of its consonants.

| | | | |
|---|---|---|---|
| vat | funny | pedal | music |
| wagon | cowboy | yellow | bike |
| hated | soap | room | hurry |
| near | cab | tow | dog |
| gas | happy | leaf | comic |
| zoo | jazz | jiffy | hazy |

| | **Beginning Consonant** | **Middle Consonant** | **Ending Consonant** |
|---|---|---|---|
| p | _____ | _____ | _____ |
| d | _____ | _____ | _____ |
| b | _____ | _____ | _____ |
| l | _____ | _____ | _____ |
| m | _____ | _____ | _____ |
| s | _____ | _____ | _____ |
| r | _____ | _____ | _____ |
| n | _____ | _____ | _____ |
| g | _____ | _____ | _____ |
| t | _____ | _____ | _____ |
| z | _____ | _____ | _____ |
| f | _____ | _____ | _____ |

Name _____

 **Directions**

Say each word in the box below. Write the words that contain a hard **c** sound under the picture of the cap. Write the words that contain a soft **c** sound under the picture of the cereal.

**Rule** When the letter **c** is followed by the vowels **a**, **o**, or **u**, it has a hard sound. Hard **c** has a **k** sound. When **c** is followed by **e**, **i**, or **y**, it usually has a soft sound. Soft **c** has an **s** sound.

| | | |
|---|---|---|
| **c**at | **c**ot | **c**ut |
| la**c**e | **c**ity | fan**c**y |

| | | | | |
|---|---|---|---|---|
| grocery | doctor | candy | recess | cinema |
| decide | coat | price | cattle | corn |
| cymbal | decorate | cub | cow | celery |
| actor | cellar | palace | carriage | pencil |

© MCP All Rights Reserved.

Say the words in each box. Draw a line to connect the words that have the same **g** sound.

**Rule** When the letter **g** is followed by the vowels **a, o,** or **u,** it has a hard sound. When **g** is followed by **e, i,** or **y,** it usually has a soft sound. Soft **g** has the sound you hear at the beginning of **jam**.

| gain | got | gum |
|------|-----|------|
| age | giant | gypsy |

**1.**

page                          game

flag                          engine

**2.**

figure                          large

gold                          giraffe

**3.**

orange                          gym

sugar                          organ

**4.**

gutter                          ago

pigeon                          arrange

▶ **Directions**

Write the words from above in the correct columns.

| Hard **g** | Soft **g** |
|------------|------------|
|            |            |
|            |            |
|            |            |
|            |            |
|            |            |
|            |            |

Name _____

## ▶ Directions

Circle each word that has the soft **c** sound or the soft **g** sound.

**Rule** When the letter **c** or **g** is followed by **e**, **i**, or **y**, the **c** or **g** usually has a soft sound.

race      pa**g**e

| | | | | | |
|---|---|---|---|---|---|
| ice | can | lace | came | fancy | gym |
| gate | giant | rice | large | huge | wig |
| rage | center | celery | because | coyote | general |
| hug | city | judge | page | face | cookies |
| game | engine | dance | leg | ceiling | police |
| fence | garden | carriage | guess | magic | place |
| tag | nice | bridge | giraffe | gem | cover |

## ▶ Directions

Circle each word that has the hard sound of **c** or **g**.

1. Everyone had a good time at Carol's birthday party.

2. The guests came dressed in fancy costumes.

3. Lance was a detective who solved strange crimes.

4. Janice wore a colorful gown and an orange wig.

5. A magician did tricks and juggled cans.

6. The children played bingo and had sack races.

7. Then Carol's mother gave them cake and ice cream.

8. Carol gasped as she opened her cards and presents.

9. Curtis gave her a goldfish in a bowl.

10. Gary the cat stared at it curiously.

11. He thought he could catch it for dinner.

12. The children giggled when Gary was carried outside.

© MCP All Rights Reserved.

Fill in the circle beside the word that belongs in each sentence.

1. Alice ____ a package in the mail.                    ○ got          ○ gym
2. She was ____ that it was from Carl.                  ○ curtain      ○ certain
3. The package was ___!                                 ○ huge         ○ hug
4. Alice tried to ____ what was in it.                  ○ gem          ○ guess
5. She ____ opened the box.                             ○ cement       ○ carefully
6. A ____ red kite was inside.                          ○ giant        ○ garden
7. "I ____ believe my eyes," said Alice.                ○ cent         ○ can't
8. "I'll ____ Carl right away to thank him."            ○ call         ○ cell

**Directions**

Write the word choices listed above in the correct columns.

**9.**        Hard **c**          **10.**        Soft **c**

_____          _____

_____          _____

_____          _____

_____          _____

**11.**       Hard **g**          **12.**        Soft **g**

_____          _____

_____          _____

_____          _____

Name  _____

▶ **Directions**

Write the name of each picture.  Then circle the vowel in the word.

1.

2.

3.

4.

5.

▶ **Directions**

Say the name of each picture.  Color each picture whose name has the short sound of **a.**

6.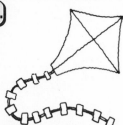

7.

8.

9.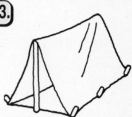

10.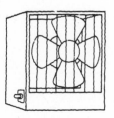

11.

12.

13.

14.

15.

16.

17.

© MCP All Rights Reserved.

Read each sentence. Circle the words with the short **a** sound, and write them on the lines. Then draw a picture to show what the sentence tells about.

**1.** Ann had fun at the beach. _____

_____

_____

**2.** She ran with her friends Vicky and Jack. _____

_____

_____

**3.** Dad helped them make two sand castles. _____

_____

_____

**4.** Then they swam fast to the raft. _____

_____

_____

**5.** They napped in the van on the ride back home. _____

_____

_____

Name _____

▶ **Directions**

Write the name of each picture. Then circle the vowel in the word.

1.
_____

2.
_____

3.
_____

4.
_____

5.
_____

6.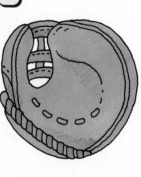
_____

7.
_____

8.
_____

▶ **Directions**

Say each word in the first column. Find a word in the second column that rhymes with it. Draw a line to connect the two words.

| 9. | | 10. | | 11. | |
|---|---|---|---|---|---|
| kick | fig | hip | tin | wig | hit |
| rip | hill | pin | big | lit | rig |
| dig | sick | pig | lip | dip | bin |
| bill | lip | did | lid | tin | tip |

© MCP All Rights Reserved.

## Directions

Say the words in the box below. Write the words that contain a short **a** sound under the picture of the cat. Write the words that contain a short **i** sound under the picture of the fish.

**Rule** If a word or syllable has only one vowel and it comes at the beginning or between two consonants, that vowel usually stands for a short sound.

    **a**nt    f**i**n

| | | | | | |
|---|---|---|---|---|---|
| lamp | late | Jim | gift | if | back |
| bike | cake | cat | ham | died | zip |
| hit | map | rain | an | sip | tick |
| ask | dime | fish | milk | ran | at |
| pin | dish | wax | will | rap | flat |

Short **a**

Short **i**

Name _____

▶ **Directions**

Write the name of each picture. Then circle the vowel in each word.

1.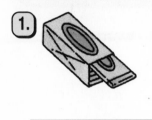
_____

2.
_____

3.
_____

4.
_____

5.
_____

6.
_____

7.
_____

8.
_____

▶ **Directions**

Fill in the circle beside the word that belongs in each sentence. Write the word on the line.

9. _____ is a very large duck.

○ Gas
○ Gus
○ Got

10. He likes to sleep in the _____ .

○ sick
○ sun
○ sad

11. One day he tried to swim in a _____ .

○ tan
○ tub
○ tent

12. It was too small so he got _____ .

○ stick
○ stuck
○ stack

13. What bad _____ for a very large duck!

○ luck
○ lick
○ lock

© MCP All Rights Reserved.

Say each word. Change the short **u** to short **a**. Write the new word in the first column. Then change the short **a** to short **i**. Write the new word in the second column.

|  | Short **a** word | Short **i** word |
|---|---|---|
| 1. fun | fan | fin |
| 2. us | | |
| 3. bug | | |
| 4. hum | | |
| 5. hut | | |
| 6. but | | |
| 7. luck | | |
| 8. tuck | | |
| 9. bun | | |
| 10. lump | | |
| 11. sung | | |
| 12. rug | | |
| 13. must | | |
| 14. stuck | | |
| 15. truck | | |
| 16. sunk | | |

**18** Lesson 9: Short vowels A, I, and U

Name _____

▶ **Directions**

Write the name of each picture. Then circle the vowel in the word.

1. _____

2. _____

3. _____

4. _____

5. _____

6. _____

7. _____

8. _____

▶ **Directions**

Read the paragraph. Underline the words with the short **o** sound. Then write those words on the lines.

### A Summer Picnic

Last summer the Todd family went on a picnic. It was a warm day, but not too hot. They had a pot of beans, hamburgers, and juice. After lunch Dot helped Mom find some shiny rocks. They put them into the bottom of a box. Bobby, the baby, went with Dad to watch the ducks by the pond. They saw a little toad hop in the grass. The family had a lot of fun that day.

9. _____

10. _____

11. _____

12. _____

13. _____

14. _____

15. _____

16. _____

17. _____

18. _____

19. _____

20. _____

21. _____

22. _____

23. _____

© MCP All Rights Reserved.

Make two new words by changing the vowel in each word to **a, i, u,** or **o.**

1. cat _____ _____   2. bad _____ _____

3. tip _____ _____   4. lock _____ _____

5. on _____ _____   6. big _____ _____

7. ham _____ _____   8. fun _____ _____

▶ **Directions**

Find the word in the box that will finish each sentence. Write the word on the line.

9. I love my tabby _____ Max.

10. He sleeps _____ the rug in my room.

11. Sometimes Max plays with a _____ .

12. He likes to _____ in and out of it.

13. I gave _____ some string to play with, too.

14. It was _____ to see Max try to catch it.

15. Once he was very _____ .

16. Max jumped on _____ of the counter.

17. He made some milk _____ over.

18. I was going to _____ the floor.

19. Then Max started to _____ up the milk.

20. He cleaned up the mess _____ a hurry!

| on |
|---|
| bag |
| mop |
| him |
| lick |
| run |
| cat |
| bad |
| tip |
| fun |
| top |
| in |

Name _____

1.

2.

3.

4.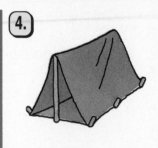

▶ **Directions**

Circle the name of each picture.

5.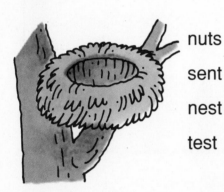
   nuts
   sent
   nest
   test

6. **10**
   test
   tent
   ten
   net

7.
   net
   ten
   nut
   not

8.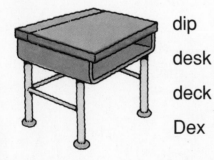
   dip
   desk
   deck
   Dex

9.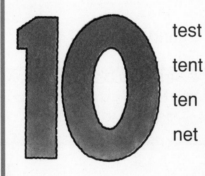
   let
   pat
   get
   jet

10.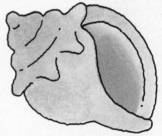
    ship
    shell
    bell
    shall

© MCP All Rights Reserved.

Find the word in the box that will finish each sentence. Write the word on the line.

1. Tomorrow I will _____ up early.

2. My dog is going to be in the _____ show.

3. The show will be in a big _____.

4. Four _____ will be the judges.

5. They will wear _____ and green badges.

6. Ben's cat will ring a _____.

7. Meg's parrot will count to _____.

8. It might even stand on one _____.

9. My dog will sit up and _____.

10. We all hope our pets do _____.

| |
|---|
| ten |
| pet |
| get |
| beg |
| tent |
| well |
| men |
| bell |
| red |
| leg |

**Directions**

Say each word. Write two rhyming words for it. The beginning letters will help you.

11. beg

p _____

l _____

12. pet

g _____

w _____

13. hen

m _____

p _____

14. bell

f _____

s _____

15. bed

r _____

l _____

16. met

b _____

l _____

Name _____

© MCP All Rights Reserved.

## ▶ Directions

Make three new words from each word at the left. For each word, use the beginning consonant, ending consonant, or vowel shown in ( ). Write the new words on the lines.

| | New Beginning Consonant | New Ending Consonant | New Vowel |
|---|---|---|---|
| 1. pen | (h) _____ | _____ (t) | ___ (i) ___ |
| 2. not | (g) _____ | _____ (d) | ___ (u) ___ |
| 3. pot | (n) _____ | _____ (d) | ___ (i) ___ |
| 4. bat | (f) _____ | _____ (d) | ___ (i) ___ |
| 5. pet | (g) _____ | _____ (g) | ___ (o) ___ |
| 6. run | (b) _____ | _____ (g) | ___ (a) ___ |
| 7. man | (c) _____ | _____ (p) | ___ (e) ___ |
| 8. bad | (h) _____ | _____ (g) | ___ (i) ___ |
| 9. ham | (j) _____ | _____ (d) | ___ (i) ___ |
| 10. big | (w) _____ | _____ (t) | ___ (e) ___ |
| 11. cup | (p) _____ | _____ (b) | ___ (a) ___ |
| 12. sat | (h) _____ | _____ (d) | ___ (i) ___ |
| 13. top | (h) _____ | _____ (t) | ___ (a) ___ |
| 14. hum | (g) _____ | _____ (g) | ___ (a) ___ |
| 15. let | (m) _____ | _____ (d) | ___ (o) ___ |

Name _____

**Rule** If a one-syllable word has two vowels, the first vowel usually stands for the long sound, and the second vowel is silent. If the first vowel is **a,** the word has the long **a** sound.

**cake**    tr**ai**n    h**ay**

1.
mail
maze
make
man

2.
ran
rain
rake
rail

3.
stay
stamp
strain
spray

4.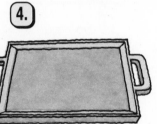
trade
trail
traffic
tray

5.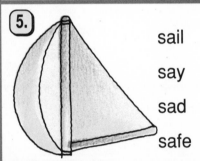
sail
say
sad
safe

6.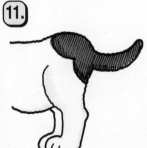
cape
cane
case
can

7.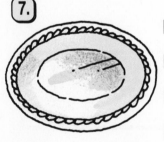
plant
plate
plane
pain

8.
race
raft
rain
rare

9.
tape
tap
plate
pat

10.
ray
train
ran
take

11.
tail
tan
tame
tape

12.
hail
day
had
hay

© MCP All Rights Reserved.

Lesson 13: Long vowel A    **25**

**▶ Directions**

Read each sentence.  Underline the words with the long **a** sound.  Then write them on the lines below the sentence.

1.  Kate could hardly wait until the first of May.

    _____  _____  _____

2.  She and Gail would see their first baseball game.

    _____  _____  _____

3.  The Braves would play the Bluejays.

    _____  _____  _____

4.  When the day finally came, it looked like rain.

    _____  _____  _____

5.  Mother told the girls to take their gray capes.

    _____  _____  _____

6.  They arrived late and paid at the gate.

    _____  _____  _____

7.  They raced to claim their places.

    _____  _____  _____

8.  A batter named Dave got on first base.

    _____  _____  _____

9.  He waved when he made it to home plate.

    _____  _____  _____

Name _____

▶ **Directions**

Circle the word that names each picture.

**Rule** If one syllable has two vowels, the first vowel usually stands for the long sound, and the second vowel is silent. If the first vowel is **i**, the word has the long **i** sound.

b**i**k**e**      d**i**m**e**      p**i**e

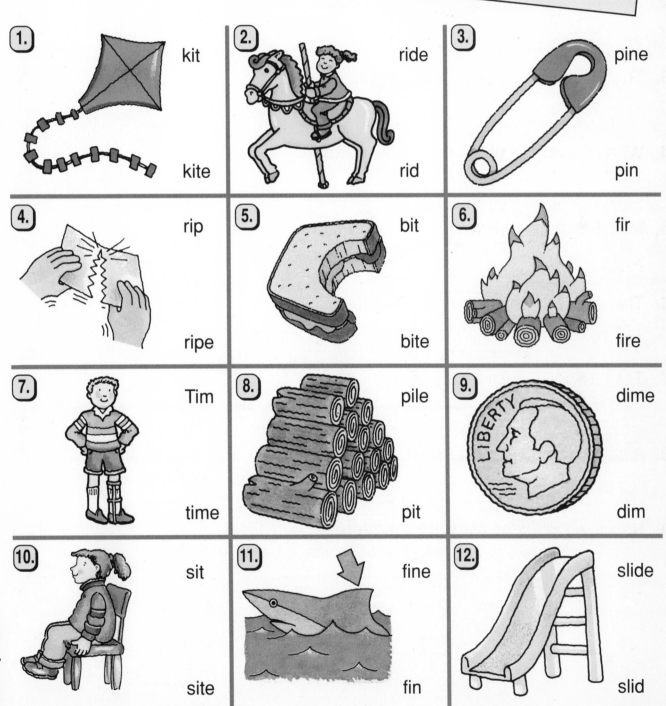

1. kit / kite

2. ride / rid

3. pine / pin

4. rip / ripe

5. bit / bite

6. fir / fire

7. Tim / time

8. pile / pit

9. dime / dim

10. sit / site

11. fine / fin

12. slide / slid

© MCP All Rights Reserved.

Find the word in the box that will finish each sentence. Write the word on the line.

1. Kay got a new _____ to fly.

2. It came in the _____ from Mike.

3. A grin lit up Kay's _____.

4. The kite had blue and red _____.

5. It had _____ yellow stars.

6. It also had a long _____.

7. Kay had to _____ a string on it.

8. She flew it on a very windy _____.

9. When the wind stopped, the kite _____ down.

10. Then it began to _____, and Kay ran home.

11. She carefully put the kite _____.

12. Kay _____ as she thought of flying it again.

| mail |
|------|
| day |
| kite |
| tail |
| smiled |
| came |
| tie |
| stripes |
| away |
| face |
| five |
| rain |

**Directions**

Circle each word that has a long vowel sound.

| whale | pie | pail | big | pig | fine |
|-------|-------|-------|------|------|-------|
| jam | blame | nine | bike | dime | gas |
| hit | save | fist | pipe | trip | man |
| sand | mice | plate | fish | cat | trash |
| ate | name | dish | five | game | snap |
| ran | hand | map | rain | pain | line |

Name _____

▶ **Directions**

Look at the picture. Circle the word that names the picture. Then complete the sentence by writing the word on the line.

**Rule** If one syllable has two vowels, the first vowel usually stands for the long sound, and the second vowel is silent. If the first vowel is **u**, the word has the long **u** sound.

t**u**b**e**     g**lue**     f**ruit**

| | | | |
|---|---|---|---|
| 1. | | flunk<br>flute | Luke will play his _____ in a concert. |
| 2. | | sun<br>Sue | He will play a song with _____ . |
| 3. | | tune<br>ton | They will play a popular _____ . |
| 4. | | sit<br>suit | Luke's mom will buy him a new _____ . |
| 5. | | cut<br>cute | Then Luke will get his hair _____ . |
| 6. | | hug<br>huge | After the recital, Dad will _____ him. |
| 7. | | fun<br>fruit | Then Luke will have _____ juice and cookies. |

© MCP All Rights Reserved.

Say each word in the box and listen for the long vowel sounds. Write the words in the correct column.

| tune | dime | stay | ride | mule | fine |
| lake | pail | use | tape | lie | came |
| pie | suit | tuba | like | cube | rain |

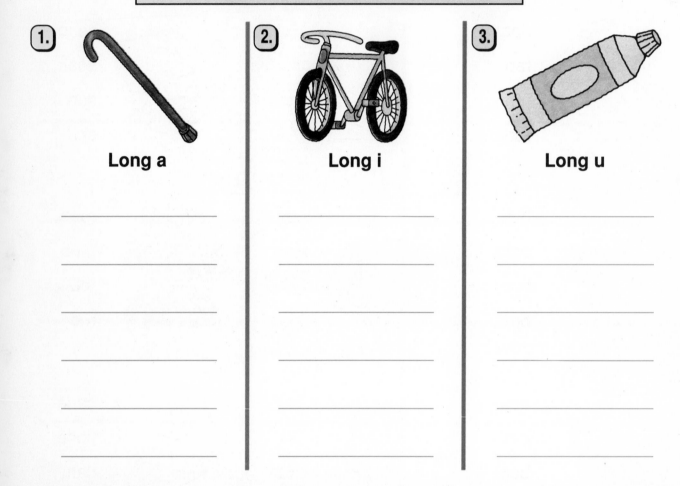

**1.** Long a

**2.** Long i

**3.** Long u

▶ **Directions**

Say each word. Write two words that rhyme with it.

**4.** lake

**5.** like

**6.** suit

Name _____

**Rule** If one syllable has two vowels, the first vowel usually stands for the long sound, and the second vowel is silent. If the first vowel is **o**, the word has the long **o** sound.

b**o**ne      g**oa**t      t**oe**

1.
   ripe
   rap
   rope
   rode

2.
   row
   ray
   rod
   rule

3.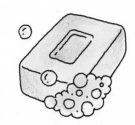
   soap
   soak
   sap
   sip

4.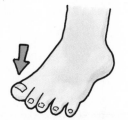
   bow
   bone
   bun
   box

5.
   tied
   tone
   time
   toad

6.
   robe
   rope
   rob
   rod

7.
   bone
   bat
   boat
   bite

8.
   tone
   toe
   toad
   tie

9.
   cane
   cone
   can
   came

10.
    doe
    den
    dock
    duck

11.
    corn
    cook
    coat
    cube

12.
    got
    goal
    game
    gas

© MCP All Rights Reserved.

Say each word. Find the word in the box that rhymes with it, and write the word on the line.

**1.**

| cone | coat | row |
|------|------|-----|
| rode | hope | pole |

load _____

boat _____

hoe _____

bone _____

soap _____

hole _____

**2.**

| pail | late | made |
|------|------|------|
| lake | way | save |

wait _____

day _____

sale _____

cake _____

paid _____

wave _____

**3.**

| like | hive | ride |
|------|------|------|
| mine | bite | pie |

dive _____

lie _____

line _____

bike _____

tied _____

kite _____

**4.**

| tune | tube | mule |
|------|------|------|
| rude | cute | use |

June _____

rule _____

mute _____

cube _____

fuse _____

dude _____

Name _____

Look at the picture. Circle the word that names the picture. Then complete the sentence by writing the word on the line.

**Rule** If one syllable has two vowels, the first vowel usually stands for the long sound, and the second vowel is silent. If the first vowel is **e**, the word has the long **e** sound.

**Pete**    **leaf**    **jeep**

| | | |
|---|---|---|
| 1. | Pet <br> Pete | _____ likes to visit the zoo. |
| 2. | seals <br> sells | He thinks the _____ are funny. |
| 3. | set <br> seat | Pete finds a _____ to watch them play. |
| 4. | tent <br> teeth | He likes the lion with its big _____ . |
| 5. | meat <br> met | The lion likes to eat _____ . |
| 6. | eagle <br> enter | Pete's favorite animal is the _____ . |
| 7. | trend <br> tree | It sits up high in a _____ . |
| 8. | fell <br> feet | Pete's _____ hurt at the end of the day. |

© MCP All Rights Reserved.

Lesson 17: Long vowel E    **33**

Say the name of each picture. Color the animals whose names contain the long vowel sound shown in the box.

**1.**

**Long a**

| jay | snail | cat | whale |

**2.**

**Long i**

| tiger | mice | kitten | pig |

**3.**

**Long u**

| skunk | mule | duck | puppy |

**4.**

**Long o**

| fox | goat | doe | ox |

**5.**

**Long e**

| seal | hen | bee | eagle |

Name _____

© MCP All Rights Reserved.

▶ **Directions**

Say the name of each picture. Then write its name on the line.

1.

_____

2.

_____

3.

_____

4.

_____

5.

_____

6.

_____

7.

_____

8.

_____

▶ **Directions**

Say each word. Change it to a word with a long vowel sound. Write the new word on the line.

9. cap _____

10. ran _____

11. tap _____

12. tub _____

13. cub _____

14. hug _____

15. got _____

16. hop _____

17. fed _____

18. hid _____

19. set _____

20. kit _____

21. can _____

22. bit _____

23. led _____

Say the first word in each row. Fill in the circle beside the word that has the same vowel sound.

1. **can** ○ mail ○ gas ○ name ○ tape

2. **rust** ○ suit ○ mule ○ hum ○ use

3. **deep** ○ peak ○ went ○ sled ○ elf

4. **milk** ○ pipe ○ hike ○ file ○ hill

5. **cute** ○ nuts ○ fuse ○ shut ○ dull

6. **clock** ○ cone ○ goat ○ dot ○ soak

7. **desk** ○ peel ○ neck ○ leap ○ tree

8. **last** ○ cake ○ rain ○ sand ○ same

9. **fire** ○ hid ○ ship ○ fill ○ kite

10. **job** ○ plot ○ note ○ soap ○ rode

11. **mug** ○ glue ○ cube ○ flute ○ luck

12. **flake** ○ black ○ race ○ ask ○ fan

13. **will** ○ mist ○ shine ○ white ○ dime

14. **send** ○ seen ○ meat ○ bet ○ jeep

15. **joke** ○ box ○ spot ○ rock ○ coat

Name

## Detective Carlos, at Your Service

"A young monkey has escaped from Paradise Park. His name is Pete and he's small and gray. Pete has a long black tail. We need help in bringing him home!"

"Let's play detectives and find Pete," Carlos said to his sister Celia. "Where would a monkey like to be? I know. Monkeys like to be up high."

1

FOLD

© MCP All Rights Reserved.

"Well," said Carlos, "if I had played hard in the trees and had eaten popcorn and peanuts, where would I be?"

Do you know where the monkey is? Write an ending for the story.

4

"Monkeys like to climb trees. I bet he's here somewhere," said Carlos.

"If the birds can't get out, how could the monkey get in?" asked Celia.

"You're right. Let's check the trees outside," said Carlos. "Look, there's a parrot. I'll ask him."

"Hi. Have you seen a cute little monkey with a long black tail?" Carlos asked.

"Polly want a cracker," said the parrot.

"That's it!" said Carlos. "I bet the monkey is hungry. Aha! See that popcorn cart?"

"No, he's not here," said Celia, "but look at this. Where does this trail go?"

Name  _____

▶ **Directions**

Say each word.  Write the two words that make up the compound word on the lines.

**Rule** A **compound word** is made up of two or more words joined together to make a new word.

**Homework** is **work** you do at **home**.

**1.** railway _____ _____

**2.** sunshine _____ _____

**3.** playmate _____ _____

**4.** beehive _____ _____

**5.** beanbag _____ _____

**6.** pancake _____ _____

**7.** wayside _____ _____

**8.** airway _____ _____

**9.** necktie _____ _____

**10.** milkweed _____ _____

**11.** peanuts _____ _____

**12.** treetop _____ _____

**13.** waterfall _____ _____

**14.** overcoat _____ _____

© MCP All Rights Reserved.

▶ **Directions**

Look at the compound words in the box. Read the clues. Match each compound word to its clue by writing its letter in the box beside the clue.

| | | | |
|---|---|---|---|
| **a.** raincoat | **b.** peanut | **c.** sailboat | **d.** playtime |
| **e.** bedtime | **f.** fireplace | **g.** paintbrush | **h.** backpack |
| **i.** rowboat | **j.** rattlesnake | **k.** mailbox | **l.** playmate |
| **m.** postcard | **n.** dustpan | **o.** outside | **p.** teapot |
| **q.** bathtub | **r.** seashell | **s.** weekend | **t.** snowflake |
| **u.** beehive | **v.** grapefruit | **w.** treetop | **x.** nightgown |
| **y.** doghouse | **z.** hillside | | |

1. the end of the week ☐

2. someone to play with ☐

3. not in the house ☐

4. a boat you can row ☐

5. a brush for painting ☐

6. time to go to bed ☐

7. a small piece of snow ☐

8. a time to play ☐

9. a pack for your back ☐

10. a large fruit with yellow skin ☐

11. the top of a tree ☐

12. a home for a dog ☐

13. a pan for dust ☐

14. a pot for tea ☐

15. a home for bees ☐

16. a coat for the rain ☐

17. a tub for a bath ☐

18. a place for a fire ☐

19. a small nut in a shell ☐

20. a boat moved by wind ☐

21. a box for mail ☐

22. a shell near the sea ☐

23. a dress worn to bed ☐

24. the side of a hill ☐

25. a card that goes in the mail ☐

26. a snake with a rattle ☐

Name _____

© MCP All Rights Reserved.

## ▶ Directions

Say the name of each picture. In the box below it, write the number of syllables you hear in the picture name.

**Hint** Words are made of syllables. You hear one vowel sound in each syllable.

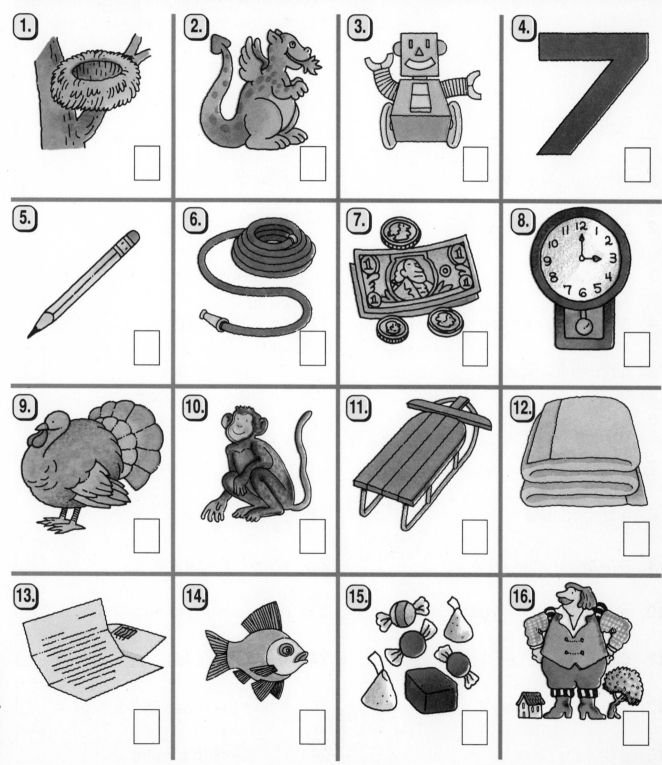

Look at each word. Write the number of vowels you **see** in the first column. Say the word. Write the number of vowels you **hear** in the second column.

**Hint** If you hear one vowel sound, the word has one syllable. If you hear two vowel sounds, the word has two syllables.

pen    pencil

| | Vowels | | | | Vowels | |
|---|---|---|---|---|---|---|
| | See | Hear | | | See | Hear |
| 1. basement | ____ | ____ | | 16. basket | ____ | ____ |
| 2. jeep | ____ | ____ | | 17. wagon | ____ | ____ |
| 3. milk | ____ | ____ | | 18. mitten | ____ | ____ |
| 4. rabbit | ____ | ____ | | 19. pancake | ____ | ____ |
| 5. pencil | ____ | ____ | | 20. visit | ____ | ____ |
| 6. music | ____ | ____ | | 21. kit | ____ | ____ |
| 7. beans | ____ | ____ | | 22. cannot | ____ | ____ |
| 8. hillside | ____ | ____ | | 23. cabin | ____ | ____ |
| 9. mailbox | ____ | ____ | | 24. sailboat | ____ | ____ |
| 10. peanuts | ____ | ____ | | 25. race | ____ | ____ |
| 11. picnic | ____ | ____ | | 26. Pete | ____ | ____ |
| 12. ate | ____ | ____ | | 27. pie | ____ | ____ |
| 13. sidetrack | ____ | ____ | | 28. beanbag | ____ | ____ |
| 14. pail | ____ | ____ | | 29. treetop | ____ | ____ |
| 15. tune | ____ | ____ | | 30. rode | ____ | ____ |

Name _____

© MCP All Rights Reserved.

▶ **Directions**

Write the name of each picture. Circle the **r** blend that stands for the beginning sound in its name.

**Rule** A **consonant blend** is two or more consonants that come together in a word. Their sounds blend together, but each sound is heard. Listen for the **r** blends in the following words.

**gr**ass      **cr**y

1.

_____

2.

_____

3.

_____

4.

_____

5.

_____

6.

_____

▶ **Directions**

Find the word or words in the box that will complete each sentence. Write the words on the lines.

| prize | try | from | brother |
|-------|-----|------|---------|
| friends | Friday | dream | proud |
| trumpet | practice | crowds | grand |

7. My _____ Tim and I play in the school band.

8. We both play the _____ .

9. We _____ every day for the parade on _____ .

10. There will be a _____ _____ for the best band.

11. We _____ of winning it.

12. _____ of people will watch _____ the sidewalks.

13. All our _____ will cheer for us.

14. We will _____ hard to make them _____ of us.

Lesson 22: R blends    **43**

▶ **Directions**

Read each riddle. Find the word in the box that answers the riddle. Write the word on the line.

| | | | | |
|---|---|---|---|---|
| frame | crow | broom | bridge | grapes |
| train | truck | drum | grasshopper | bride |

**1.** You can cross over me.

I am a _____ .

**2.** Drive me on the road.

I am a _____ .

**3.** I hold a picture.

I am a _____ .

**4.** I am a big black bird.

I am a _____ .

**5.** We are fruits on the vine.

We are _____ .

**6.** You sweep the floor with me.

I am a _____ .

**7.** I ride on the tracks.

I am a _____ .

**8.** It is my wedding day.

I am a _____ .

**9.** I am a green bug.

I am a _____ .

**10.** You play me with sticks.

I am a _____ .

Name _____

▶ **Directions**

Write the name of each picture.
Circle the **l** blend that stands for
the beginning sound in its name.

**Rule** Remember that in a **consonant blend** the sounds of the consonants blend together, but each sound is heard. Listen for the **l** blends in the following words.
**bl**ack     **pl**ant

1.

_____

2.

_____

3.

_____

4.

_____

5.

_____

6.

_____

7.

_____

8.

_____

9.

_____

10.

_____

11.

_____

12.

_____

13.

_____

14.

_____

15.

_____

© MCP All Rights Reserved.

▶ **Directions**

For each word, find two words in the box with the same **l** blend. Write them on the lines.

1. black _____ _____

2. clean _____ _____

3. flat _____ _____

4. glad _____ _____

5. plant _____ _____

6. sled _____ _____

clock
blue
glow
sleep
play
flag
please
slide
clip
block
fly
glue

▶ **Directions**

Read each sentence carefully. Find the word in the box that will complete the sentence. Write the word on the line.

7. As Flora left school, the wind was _____ .

8. There were many _____ in the sky.

9. It was too cold to stop to _____ .

10. Flora _____ her hands in her pockets.

11. She had left her _____ at home.

12. Flora quickly walked the six _____ home.

13. When she got there, she was _____ .

14. Her mom gave her a _____ of warm milk.

15. Then Flora sat _____ to the fire.

slipped
glad
blocks
glass
close
blowing
play
gloves
clouds

Name _____

▶ **Directions**

Write the name of each picture. Circle the **s** blend that stands for the beginning sound in its name.

**Rule** Remember that in a **consonant blend** the sounds of the consonants blend together, but each sound is heard. Listen for the **s** blends in the following words.

**sk**id     **sp**ell

1.

_____

2.

_____

3.

_____

4.

_____

5.

_____

6.

_____

7.

_____

8.

_____

9.

_____

10.

_____

11.

_____

12.

_____

13.

_____

14.

_____

15.

_____

© MCP All Rights Reserved.

Read each sentence. Circle the word that will complete the sentence. Write the word on the line.

1. Our first camping trip was ( special,  slender ). _____

2. We ( stamp,  spent ) five days in the mountains. _____

3. Our trip was in early ( string,  spring ). _____

4. The weather was ( still,  spill ) quite chilly. _____

5. We wore ( scatters,  sweaters ) under our coats. _____

6. We also wore two pairs of ( stockings,  snails ). _____

7. I tripped on a ( stump,  sport ) while hiking. _____

8. My ankle became very ( swollen,  squirrel ). _____

9. We all ( swept,  screamed ) when we saw a snake. _____

10. The snake just ( splashed,  slithered ) away. _____

► **Directions**

Read each word. Circle the **s** blend that is used in the word. Write the word on the line.

11. s k i d _____      12. s t a m p _____

13. s m i l e _____      14. s p r a y _____

15. s c a l e _____      16. s t r e a m _____

17. s n i f f _____      18. s p e l l _____

19. s w e e p _____      20. s c r u b _____

21. s m e l l _____      22. s n o w _____

Name _____

▶ **Directions**

Sometimes consonant blends can be at the end of a word. Say the name of each picture. Circle the word that names the picture.

1. stamp     stand

2. mast     mask

3. trunk     trust

4. limp     list

5. kind     king

6. raft     ramp

7. hang     hand

8. sprint     spring

9. plank     plant

10. wing     wink

11. milk     mint

12. pomp     pond

13. desk     dent

14. sing     sink

15. gill     gift

16. shelf     send

© MCP All Rights Reserved.

▶ **Directions**

Find the word in the box that will complete each sentence. Write the word on the line.

| | | | | |
|---|---|---|---|---|
| stick | raft | glee | croaking | flying |
| string | float | sink | pond | stayed |
| spring | placed | crossed | jumped | proud |

1. Glenn built a wooden _____ .

2. He used _____ to tie it together.

3. He hoped that it would _____ on the water.

4. One day he took it to the lily _____ .

5. It was the first warm day of _____ .

6. Birds were _____ in the sky.

7. Frogs were _____ in the pond.

8. Glenn carefully _____ the raft in the water.

9. He pushed it with a _____ .

10. He _____ his fingers as he watched it.

11. Would the raft _____ under the water?

12. No, it _____ afloat.

13. Then, a frog _____ onto the raft.

14. Glenn laughed with _____ at the sight.

15. He felt very happy and _____ .

Name _____

▶ **Directions**

Add **y** to each blend to make a word. Write the word on the line.

**Rule**  When **y** is the only vowel at the end of a syllable or a word of one syllable, **y** has the long **i** sound.

sh**y**

1. fr _____

2. cr _____

3. tr _____

4. dr _____

5. sk _____

6. sl _____

7. fl _____

8. spr _____

▶ **Directions**

Read each question. Use one or more of the words you just made to answer it. Write your answer on the lines. Use a complete sentence.

**9.** Where must we look in order to see clouds?

_____

_____

**10.** Why do we use umbrellas when it rains?

_____

_____

**11.** What can an airplane do in the sky?

_____

_____

**12.** What would you do if you fell and hurt yourself?

_____

_____

© MCP All Rights Reserved.

Say each word in the box and listen for the **y** sound. Write the words in the correct column.

**Rule** When **y** is the only vowel at the end of a syllable or a word of one syllable, **y** has the long **i** sound. When **y** is the only vowel at the end of a word of more than one syllable, **y** usually has the long **e** sound.

fl**y**     cr**y**ing     prett**y**

| every | sky | swiftly | bunny |
| grocery | why | shy | trying |
| muddy | cry | | |

**Y** = Long **i**                    **Y** = Long **e**

_____        _____

_____        _____

_____        _____

_____        _____

_____        _____

▶ **Directions**

Find the word in the box that will complete each sentence. Write the word on the line.

1. My _____ likes to do things together.

2. Sometimes we go to the _____ .

3. There are so _____ books to choose from.

4. Dad likes _____ books about ancient Egypt.

5. I like books with lots of _____ jokes.

6. Mom likes books with _____ flowers in them.

7. Once we checked out more than _____ books.

8. It was difficult to _____ them!

pretty
many
library
family
carry
twenty
funny
history

Name _____

**Directions**

Say the name of each picture. Find the name in the box. Write it on the line.

| cry | party | bunny | puppy |
| baby | sky | pretty | try |
| fly | city | pony | penny |

1.
_____

2.
_____

3.
_____

4.
_____

5.
_____

6.
_____

7.
_____

8.
_____

**Directions**

Say the first word in each row. Circle the words that have the same **y** sound as that word.

**Rule** When **y** comes at the beginning of a word, **y** is a consonant.
**y**olk

| 9. | **yes** | sky | yard | yellow | windy |
| 10. | **many** | pretty | yet | dry | sweetly |
| 11. | **fly** | lovely | yell | try | why |
| 12. | **happy** | sorry | every | yard | fry |
| 13. | **year** | many | yolk | funny | yarn |

© MCP All Rights Reserved.

▶ **Directions**

Read the story.  Underline each word that has a **y**.  Write the words in the
correct column.

## The Ice-Cream Man

One afternoon my brother Craig and I heard a jet go over our yard.

"Oh, isn't it a beauty?" I asked.

"Where is it?" I heard Craig cry.

"Over there, in the sky above the yellow house," I yelled. "Do you see it yet?"

"I would like to fly a jet like that one," said Craig.

"Let's try to save so that we can have our own plane when we grow up. Here's twenty cents to start," I said.

Just then, from down the street came the jingling of a bell and the blowing of a whistle. We both knew that it was Goody, the ice-cream man. His ice-cream bars were big and thick and creamy. Craig looked at me. "Why not?" I said. "It is very hot and dry."

As we ate the ice cream, Craig said, "We'd better start soon to save for the airplane, or we'll be fifty years old before we get it."

"Yes," I said. "We'd better start early tomorrow."

| **Y** as a consonant | **Y** = Long **e** | **Y** = Long **i** |
| --- | --- | --- |
| | | |
| | | |
| | | |
| | | |
| | | |
| | | |

Name _____

© MCP All Rights Reserved.

▶ **Directions**

Write the name of each picture. Then circle the digraph in the word.

**Definition** A **consonant digraph** consists of two consonants that together represent one sound.
**kn**it

1.

_____

2.

_____

3.

_____

4.

_____

5.

_____

6.
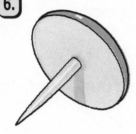
_____

7.

_____

8.

_____

▶ **Directions**

Say each word. Then circle the consonant digraph.

| | | | |
|---|---|---|---|
| 9. scheme | 10. wheel | 11. kitchen | 12. write |
| 13. birthday | 14. threw | 15. nickel | 16. peaches |
| 17. north | 18. finish | 19. mother | 20. rough |
| 21. beneath | 22. choke | 23. knit | 24. echo |
| 25. know | 26. chord | 27. thick | 28. farther |
| 29. telephone | 30. shake | 31. wrist | 32. chocolate |
| 33. bother | 34. ticket | 35. wheat | 36. chorus |
| 37. tough | 38. sign | 39. school | 40. gnaw |

Circle the word that completes each sentence.  Then write the word on the line.

1. My _____ is a good cook.  feather    father

2. He enjoys working in the _____ .  kitchen    kitten

3. Dad bakes _____ bread.  wheat    wheel

4. He also bakes _____ cookies.  chocolate    chalk

5. He makes fancy _____cakes.  birthday    birds

6. One is decorated with fresh _____ .  sheds    cherries

7. Once my _____ held a Hobby Day.  schooner    school

8. Dad _____ his best recipes.  shared    shaved

9. Everyone _____ he was great.  though    thought

10. We wanted him to _____ how
    we felt.  know    now

11. So we _____ him letters.  wrist    wrote

12. Dad _____ when he read them.  laughed    rough

Name _____

Find the word in the box that will complete the sentence. Write the word on the line.

1. I like riding the _____ bus this year.

2. My classroom _____ is very nice.

3. Her name is Ms. _____ .

4. She _____ how to make learning fun.

5. Now I even like doing _____ problems.

6. Once I was sick with a bad _____ .

7. My _____ made me stay in bed.

8. My teacher _____ me a letter.

9. Everyone in class _____ it.

10. Someone drew a picture of an _____ on it.

11. The picture made me _____ .

12. I _____ it was very funny.

| laugh |
|---|
| cough |
| school |
| White |
| elephant |
| mother |
| knows |
| thought |
| signed |
| math |
| wrote |
| teacher |

**Directions**

Say each word. Write its consonant digraph on the line.

13. rough _____    14. kitchen _____    15. Ralph _____

16. choice _____    17. wrong _____    18. tough _____

19. know _____    20. chemical _____    21. sign _____

22. gnaw _____    23. knife _____    24. patch _____

25. phone _____    26. wrist _____    27. Kathy _____

© MCP All Rights Reserved.

## Directions

Say each word and circle its consonant digraph. Write the word in the column that tells whether the consonant digraph is heard at the beginning, in the middle, or at the end of the word.

| | | | | |
|---|---|---|---|---|
| beach | another | path | chin | elephant |
| threw | sheep | dishes | brush | wheel |
| write | matches | laughed | white | whine |
| north | birthday | with | tough | chorus |
| cough | peaches | know | wish | sign |
| together | mother | catch | rather | choose |

| Beginning | Middle | End |
|---|---|---|
| | | |

Name _____

**Directions**

Read each sentence. Fill in the circle below the word that correctly completes the sentence. Write the word on the line.

1. The third _____ were very excited.    graders ○    traders ○

2. They were going on a _____ to the zoo.    slip ○    trip ○

3. Everyone hoped for a _____ sunny day.    bright ○    slight ○

4. The bus ride seemed very _____.    slow ○    flow ○

5. _____ they arrived, the zoo was crowded.    When ○    Chew ○

6. The teacher told them to _____ together.    shovel ○    stay ○

7. The _____ enjoyed each exhibit.    throne ○    children ○

8. Frank liked watching the _____.    wrinkles ○    dolphins ○

9. Jay was _____ with the polar bears.    thrilled ○    thirty ○

10. Mandy had peanuts in her _____.    know ○    knapsack ○

11. She fed them to the _____.    eleventh ○    elephants ○

12. Luis stared at the _____.    flamingos ○    flats ○

13. He had never seen such pink _____.    together ○    feathers ○

14. It was soon time for the zoo to _____.    close ○    chose ○

15. The children headed back to _____.    spring ○    school ○

© MCP All Rights Reserved.

| | | | |
|---|---|---|---|
| 1. sheep | 2. match | 3. tough | 4. lunch |
| 5. dishes | 6. finish | 7. elephant | 8. these |
| 9. knew | 10. wren | 11. sign | 12. check |
| 13. choke | 14. this | 15. punch | 16. telephone |
| 17. gnat | 18. pinch | 19. shut | 20. thrush |
| 21. phase | 22. birthday | 23. knee | 24. whisper |
| 25. enough | 26. wheel | 27. shop | 28. chart |

▶ **Directions**

Circle each word that has a consonant digraph. Write the words you circled on the lines.

29. Nick shot out of bed. _____ _____

30. He checked his watch. _____ _____

31. Then he took a shower. _____ _____

32. He brushed his teeth. _____ _____

33. He threw on his shirt. _____ _____

34. The telephone rang. _____ _____

35. Father picked it up. _____ _____

36. He spoke with the caller. _____ _____

37. Then he said, "Thank you." _____ _____

38. He told Nick who it was. _____ _____

39. It was Coach Smith. _____ _____

40. The track meet was canceled. _____ _____

Name _____

▶ **Directions**

Look at the name of each picture. In the first box under the name, write the number of vowels you see in the word. Say the name of each picture. In the second box, write the number of vowel sounds you hear. In the third box, write the number of syllables in the word. The first one is done for you.

1. telephone
[4] [3] [3]

2. wheat
[ ] [ ] [ ]

3. sandwich
[ ] [ ] [ ]

4. spider
[ ] [ ] [ ]

5. chicks
[ ] [ ] [ ]

6. elephant
[ ] [ ] [ ]

7. fish
[ ] [ ] [ ]

8. umbrella
[ ] [ ] [ ]

9. slippers
[ ] [ ] [ ]

10. truck
[ ] [ ] [ ]

11. cheese
[ ] [ ] [ ]

12. propeller
[ ] [ ] [ ]

13. knife
[ ] [ ] [ ]

14. blanket
[ ] [ ] [ ]

15. wheel
[ ] [ ] [ ]

16. stove
[ ] [ ] [ ]

© MCP All Rights Reserved.

## ▶ Directions

Circle the two-syllable word that makes sense in the sentence. Write the word on the line.

1. Friday was _____ birthday.        Mother's    my        problem

2. I baked a _____ cake.             chicken     fudge     cherry

3. The cake had _____ candles.       thirty      six       forest

4. Mom loved her _____ .             presents    gifts     little

5. I _____ her a picture.            painted     drew      player

6. Dad gave her a blue _____ .       kitchen     dress     sweater

7. Grandmother _____ her
   a red scarf.                                  never       bought    knitted

## ▶ Directions

Read the poem. Then complete each sentence by writing the correct word from the poem on the line.

**Jack Be Nimble**
Jack be nimble,
Jack be quick.
Jack jump over
The candlestick.

8. A one-syllable word that means *fast* is _____ .

9. The two-syllable word in the title of the poem is _____ .

10. The three-syllable word in the poem is _____ .

11. A two-syllable word that means *above* or *across* is _____ .

Name _____

▶ **Directions**

Say the name of each picture. Circle the **ar, or, ir, ur,** or **er** in the name of each picture.

**Hint** An **r** after a vowel makes the vowel have a sound that is different from the usual long or short sound.

p**ur**se     g**ar**den

| | | |
|---|---|---|
| 1.  horn | 2.  feather | 3.  bird |
| 4.  tiger | 5.  star | 6.  nurse |
| 7.  barn | 8.  circus | 9.  turkey |

▶ **Directions**

Circle each word that contains **ar, or, ir, ur,** or **er**. Write the words you circled on the lines.

**10.** The storm was over. _____ _____

**11.** Sam hurried into the garden. _____ _____

**12.** He was worried about his turtle. _____ _____

**13.** The thunder might have scared it. _____ _____

**14.** Sam looked for it carefully. _____ _____

**15.** It was sleeping under a flower. _____ _____

© MCP All Rights Reserved.

Find the word in the box that will complete the sentence. Write the word on the line.

| weather | for | favorite | forth | warm | started | dark |
|---------|-----|----------|-------|------|---------|------|
| birds | park | Hurry | soccer | storm | Saturday | thunder |

1. Jane likes to play at the _____ .

2. She meets her friends there every _____ .

3. Their _____ game is baseball.

4. Sometimes they play _____ , too.

5. They play games _____ hours.

6. One day the _____ changed.

7. The sky got _____ and cloudy.

8. The wind made the trees sway back

   and _____ .

9. Loud _____ rumbled in the distance.

10. The _____ found shelter in the trees.

11. Jane _____ to run as it began to rain.

12. "_____!" she called to her friends.

13. They raced home through the windy _____ .

14. They couldn't wait to get dry and _____ .

Name _____

▶ **Directions**

Circle the **ar, or, ir, ur,** or **er** in each word. Then find the word in the box that has the same beginning letter and vowel sound. Write it on the line.

| purse | thirty | first | hurdle | bore | bark | leader |
|-------|--------|-------|--------|------|------|--------|
| cord | dart | girlfriend | Burt | startle | neither | shore |

**1.** f i r _____

**2.** b u r n _____

**3.** l e t t e r _____

**4.** c o r n _____

**5.** h u r t _____

**6.** g i r l _____

**7.** d a r k _____

**8.** s t a r _____

**9.** b o r n _____

**10.** s h o r t _____

**11.** t h i r d _____

**12.** n e v e r _____

**13.** b a r n _____

**14.** p u r p l e _____

▶ **Directions**

Find the word in the box that will complete the sentence. Write the word on the line.

| third | sparkled | bursting | mother | garden | summer | orange |
|-------|----------|----------|--------|--------|--------|--------|

**15.** My _____ has a green thumb.

**16.** She loves to work in her _____ .

**17.** Our backyard is beautiful during the _____ .

**18.** It is _____ with colorful flowers!

**19.** There are _____ and yellow and pink flowers.

**20.** Mom once won _____ place at a flower show.

**21.** Her eyes _____ as she received her prize.

© MCP All Rights Reserved.

▶ **Directions**

Read the sentences. Underline each word that contains **ar, or, ir, ur**, or **er**. Then write the words you underlined in the correct boxes below.

1. Rita made a special birthday card for a friend.
2. First she decorated it with blue and red stars.
3. Then she wrote a clever little verse.
4. In the morning, Rita hurried to the mailbox.
5. Darla received many surprises on Friday.
6. Mom and Dad gave her a purse, a curling brush, and a red sweater.
7. She got a yellow bird from Aunt Shirley.
8. She really liked the large and colorful greeting from Rita.

ir

er

or

ar

ur

Name _____

▶ **Directions**

Say the name of each picture. In the box write the number of syllables you hear in the picture name. Then color the pictures whose names have two syllables.

**Hint** The letters **ar, or, ir, ur,** and **er** each have one vowel sound. A word has as many syllables as it has vowel sounds.

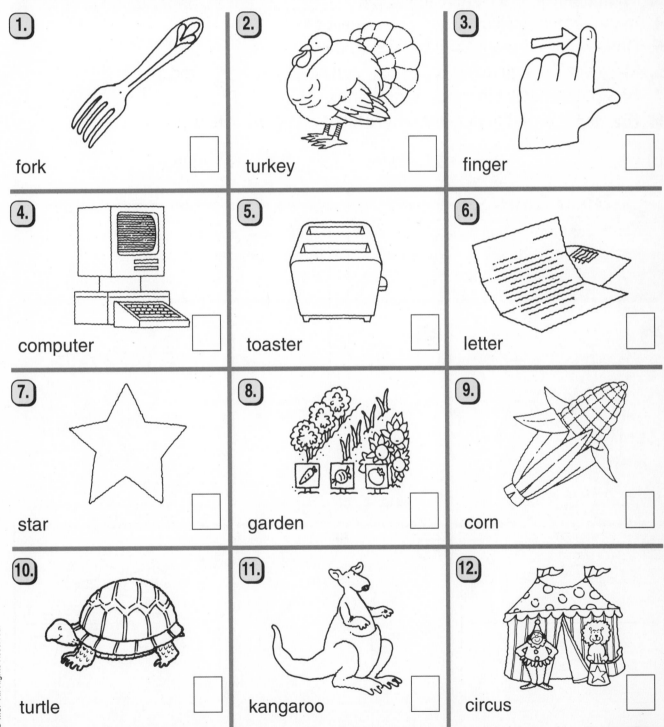

1. fork

2. turkey

3. finger

4. computer

5. toaster

6. letter

7. star

8. garden

9. corn

10. turtle

11. kangaroo

12. circus

© MCP All Rights Reserved.

## ▶ Directions

Say each word. Write the number of syllables you hear.

1. shortly _____
2. factory _____
3. dirty _____
4. popcorn _____
5. thirsty _____
6. storm _____
7. Saturday _____
8. carpet _____
9. dangerous _____
10. part _____
11. fern _____
12. yesterday _____
13. turkey _____
14. feather _____
15. carving _____
16. garden _____
17. thunder _____
18. father _____
19. third _____
20. burn _____
21. purple _____

## ▶ Directions

Write the name of each picture. Color the picture blue if its name has one syllable, yellow if its name has two syllables, or green if its name has three syllables.

**22.**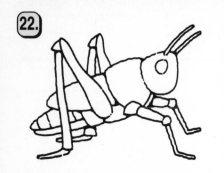

_____

**23.**

_____

**24.**

_____

**25.**

_____

**26.**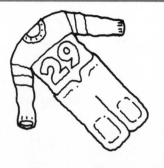

_____

**27.**

_____

Name _____

▶ **Directions**

Draw a line from a syllable in the first column to a syllable in the second column to make a word. Write the word on the line.

**1.**

pur    per      _____purple_____

lan    ple      _____

pa     tern     _____

car    ton      _____

**2.**

thir    kle      _____

spar   ty       _____

nev    form    _____

plat    er       _____

**3.**

Mar    ing      _____

der    by       _____

morn   ger      _____

fin     vin      _____

**4.**

sis     tha      _____

gar    ter      _____

Mar    son      _____

per    den      _____

**5.**

tur    corn     _____

sup    key      _____

thir    per      _____

pop    ty       _____

**6.**

ti      pet      _____

car    der      _____

ar     ger      _____

thun   my       _____

**7.**

slip    ter      _____

af     way      _____

stair    per      _____

birth   day      _____

**8.**

lad    ger      _____

re     port     _____

tur    der      _____

gin    nip      _____

© MCP All Rights Reserved.

## ▶ Directions

Read each riddle and choose a word from the box that answers it. Write the word on the line. Then write the number of syllables you hear in the word in the small box.

| squirrel | purple | Saturday | short | yesterday |
|---|---|---|---|---|
| thirteen | birthday | Thursday | farmer | turtle |

**1.** What do we call the day before Friday?

**2.** Which animal has a hard shell on its back?

**3.** Which number comes after 12 and before 14?

**4.** Which word means the opposite of <u>tall</u>?

**5.** What do we call the day on which a person is born?

**6.** What do we call the day before today?

**7.** Which animal has a bushy tail and eats acorns and nuts?

**8.** What do we call a person who grows crops on the land?

**9.** What do we call the day before Sunday?

**10.** Which color do we get by mixing red and blue paint?

Name _____

**Prairie Dogs: Above and Below the Ground**

What does a dog's house look like? You might change your answer if it's a prairie dog's house. These critters are ground squirrels. Does that give you a clue?

Prairie dogs live in dark tunnels, or burrows, under the earth. They are friendly creatures, so they dig their burrows in "dog towns."

1

© MCP All Rights Reserved.

Tender green grass makes a good meal for prairie dogs. They also like many other kinds of plants. For a special lunch, they just may munch on a crunchy grasshopper!

Make up a story about a prairie dog. Can you think of one problem the prairie dog might have? Show how it solves its problem.

4

Prairie dog pups are born in a burrow. They may have five or six brothers and sisters. At first all they do is eat, grow, and play. They nibble and gnaw. They play chase and catch.

After a while, they are ready to climb up from their burrow to find out about such things as sunshine and grass.

Why does a prairie dog tunnel always have at least two doors? One reason is to let fresh air flow in. The other reason is in case of trouble.

If a prairie dog senses danger, it barks an urgent warning bark. The dogs that have strayed from their burrows are alert for this bark. They scurry back into the nearest hole.

FOLD

Lesson 36: Fold-up Book: Reviewing R-controlled vowels, blends, and digraphs

Name _____

▶ **Directions**

Read each contraction. Write the two words that make each contraction. Then write the letter or letters that were left out.

**Definition**  A **contraction** is a short way of writing two words. It is formed by putting two words together and leaving out one or more letters. Use an apostrophe (') to show where something is left out.

I am = I'm        we will = we'll

| Contraction | Two Words | Letters Left Out |
|---|---|---|
| **1.** isn't | | |
| **2.** there's | | |
| **3.** haven't | | |
| **4.** wouldn't | | |
| **5.** you've | | |
| **6.** it's | | |
| **7.** let's | | |
| **8.** don't | | |
| **9.** they've | | |
| **10.** couldn't | | |
| **11.** he's | | |

© MCP All Rights Reserved.

## Directions

Find the contraction in column B for each pair of words in column A and write it on the line.

| A | B | A | B |
|---|---|---|---|
| I am | I'm | were not | it's |
| is not | isn't | would not | wouldn't |
| we are | I've | it is | weren't |
| I have | we're | did not | didn't |

| A | B | A | B |
|---|---|---|---|
| you will | let's | that is | shouldn't |
| you are | wasn't | they will | aren't |
| let us | we'll | will not | that's |
| was not | you'll | are not | they'll |
| we will | you're | should not | won't |

## Directions

Complete each sentence using a contraction from the box below.

| we'll | It's | aren't |
|---|---|---|
| won't | I've | |

1. _____ going to be a fine day for a hike.

2. _____ been looking forward to it.

3. First _____ walk through the forest.

4. I hope the trails _____ muddy.

5. We _____ get home until evening.

Name _____

▶ **Directions**

Read the story, and circle each contraction. On the lines at the bottom of the page, write the two words that make each contraction you found.

### Time for Safety

Peter and his little brother, Tom, hurried down the street on their way to school.

"I hope we're not late today," said Tom.

"We aren't late," said Peter. "If we are, they'll wait a little while for us."

"Do you think it'll rain?" asked Tom.

"We've been hoping for two weeks that it wouldn't rain," said Peter. "It couldn't rain if it wanted to. There's not a cloud in the sky."

The stop light was red as they came to the corner. Tom stepped off the curb.

"You'd better get back on the curb," said Peter. "You're not supposed to start crossing the street until the light turns green."

"Where's the policeman?" asked Tom. "If he's not here, we won't get caught."

"It doesn't matter whether someone is watching you or not. Obey the safety rules all the time, and you won't get hurt. You don't want to get hit by a car, do you?" asked his big brother. "Can't you see yourself lying in a hospital while the rest of us are out having fun? Let's wait for the light."

1. _____    2. _____    3. _____

4. _____    5. _____    6. _____

7. _____    8. _____    9. _____

10. _____   11. _____   12. _____

13. _____   14. _____   15. _____

16. _____   17. _____   18. _____

© MCP All Rights Reserved.

Write the two words that make each contraction.

1. I'm _____

2. aren't _____

3. can't _____

4. shouldn't _____

5. couldn't _____

6. didn't _____

7. he's _____

8. we'll _____

9. doesn't _____

10. let's _____

11. here's _____

12. you'll _____

13. I've _____

14. won't _____

15. you're _____

16. they've _____

17. she's _____

18. we've _____

19. I'll _____

20. it's _____

▶ **Directions**

Write a story using five of the words listed above.

_____

_____

_____

_____

_____

_____

_____

_____

_____

Name _____

▶ **Directions**

Circle the word that names each picture. Then color the pictures that show more than one.

**Rule** When **s** or **es** is added to a word it forms the plural. Plural means "more than one." See how the ending **s** or **es** makes these words mean more than one.

| one duck | two duck**s** |
| one fox | many fox**es** |

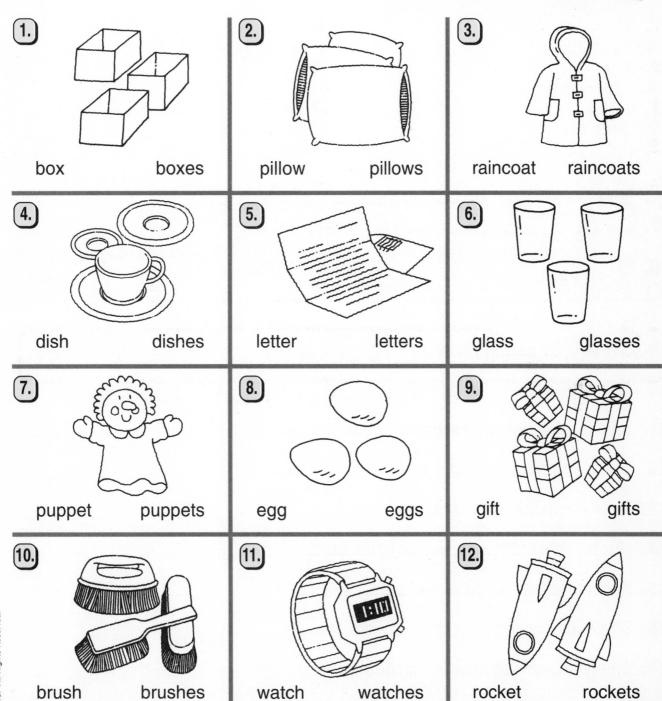

1. box     boxes

2. pillow     pillows

3. raincoat     raincoats

4. dish     dishes

5. letter     letters

6. glass     glasses

7. puppet     puppets

8. egg     eggs

9. gift     gifts

10. brush     brushes

11. watch     watches

12. rocket     rockets

© MCP All Rights Reserved.

**Rule** If a word ends in **ss, x, ch,** or **sh,** add the suffix **es** to make it mean more than one.

| | |
|---|---|
| one porch | two porch**es** |
| one class | many class**es** |
| one fox | three fox**es** |
| one brush | some brush**es** |

1. five (cross) _____
2. some (glass) _____
3. those (box) _____
4. all (six) _____
5. seven (dress) _____
6. few (church) _____
7. three (ax) _____
8. many (dish) _____

▶ **Directions**

Underline the word in each sentence that means more than one. Then write its base word on the line.

**Definition** The word to which a suffix is added is called the **base word.**

9. Kim is busy packing boxes. _____

10. She is using bunches of paper. _____

11. She carefully wraps the good dishes. _____

12. She puts paper around the glasses. _____

13. Then she packs her dresses. _____

14. Her favorite is the one with patches on it. _____

15. Kim marks her suitcase with crosses. _____

16. She does not pack her paintbrushes. _____

17. She ties them together in batches. _____

18. She needs them for her art classes. _____

Name _____

 **Directions**

Write the plural form of the word in parentheses.

**Rule** If a word ends in **y** preceded by a consonant, change the **y** to **i** and add **es**. If **y** is preceded by a vowel, just add **s**.

| one baby | two bab**ies** |
| one jay | many jay**s** |

1. three (cherry) _____

2. some (lily) _____

3. eight (fairy) _____

4. those (fly) _____

5. two (party) _____

6. nine (tray) _____

7. few (boy) _____

8. many (chimney) _____

9. four (day) _____

10. all (turkey) _____

▶ **Directions**

Underline the word in each sentence that means more than one. Then write its base word on the line.

11. Lucy went downtown to buy groceries. _____

12. She saw some puppies in a pet store window. _____

13. Two ladies worked in the store. _____

14. "May I pet the doggies?" Lucy asked. _____

15. One lady said, "They're as cute as monkeys." _____

16. "They're as stubborn as donkeys," said the other. _____

17. Lucy said, "They're as sweet as bunnies." _____

18. "They'll be sold in a few days," said the first lady. _____

19. Lucy said, "They are as bright as sun rays." _____

20. "A puppy's more fun than a ton of toys!" _____

© MCP All Rights Reserved.

 **Directions**

Look at each picture. Then read the word below the line. Change the word to mean more than one. Write the new word on the line.

**1.** **Animals**

_____
(puppy)

_____
(monkey)

_____
(turkey)

_____
(jay)

_____
(bunny)

_____
(pony)

**2.** **Flowers**

_____
(daisy)

_____
(lily)

_____
(pansy)

**3.** **People**

_____
(baby)

_____
(boy)

_____
(lady)

Lesson 40: Adding suffixes -S and -ES to words ending in Y

Name _____

© MCP All Rights Reserved.

▶ **Directions**

Write the plural form of the word in parentheses.

**Rule** If a word ends in **f** or **fe**, change the **f** or **fe** to **v** before adding the suffix **es**.

one thief     several thie**ves**
one life      nine li**ves**

1. these (leaf) _____

2. six (calf) _____

3. those (wolf) _____

4. few (knife) _____

5. four (shelf) _____

6. several (elf) _____

7. two (half) _____

8. few (wife) _____

9. ten (thief) _____

10. many (life) _____

▶ **Directions**

Write a word from the box below to complete each sentence. Then write its base word on the line.

| leaves | wolves | lives | scarves | loaves |
|--------|--------|-------|---------|--------|
| calves | knives | shelves | wives | |

11. Long ago, pioneers led hard _____ .    _____

12. The men chopped wood to make _____ .    _____

13. They built barns for the cows and _____ .    _____

14. They had to protect them from wild _____ .    _____

15. Pioneer _____ worked as hard as their husbands. _____

16. Each week they baked _____ of bread.    _____

17. They picked berries from the _____ of bushes.    _____

18. At night, the women knitted warm _____ .    _____

19. The men sharpened their _____ beside the fire.    _____

Lesson 41: Adding suffix -ES to words ending in F and FE

Read each clue. Find the word in the box that matches the clue. Then write the word in the crossword puzzle.

**Hint** **Singular** means **one**. **Plural** means **more than one**.

| ELF | THIEVES | SCARVES | FOXES | LOAVES |
| WIFE | SCARF | TURKEYS | LIVES | WOLF |
| SHELVES | AXES | ELVES | CAR | |

**Across**
1. singular form of elves
4. plural form of thief
7. plural form of scarf
9. singular form of wives
12. plural form of fox
13. plural form of turkey

**Down**
2. plural form of life
3. plural form of shelf
5. plural form of elf
6. plural form of loaf
8. singular form of scarves
9. singular form of wolves
10. plural form of ax
11. singular form of cars

Name _____

1. many (fox) _____

2. several (wish) _____

3. two (boy) _____

4. these (wax) _____

5. few (wife) _____

6. seven (patch) _____

7. four (calf) _____

8. some (kiss) _____

9. those (lily) _____

10. six (shelf) _____

▶ **Directions**

Underline the word in each sentence that means more than one. Then write its base word on the line.

11. "Take two guesses what's in each box," said Jane. _____

12. "I labeled the boxes," said Dad. _____

13. "The knives are in this box." _____

14. Jane asked, "Where are the glasses?" _____

15. "They're in here with the dishes," said Dad. _____

16. Jane and Dad put everything on the shelves. _____

17. Dad found some brushes to clean the chimney. _____

18. He used matches to light the fire. _____

19. Jane went outside to rake the leaves. _____

20. Then she picked some daisies for the table. _____

21. In a few days the new house would seem like home. _____

© MCP All Rights Reserved.

Read each word. Make new words by adding the suffixes **s, ed,** and **ing.**
Write the new words in the correct columns.

| | s | ed | ing |
|---|---|---|---|
| 1. play | | | |
| 2. jump | | | |
| 3. pick | | | |
| 4. clean | | | |
| 5. help | | | |
| 6. learn | | | |
| 7. cook | | | |

▶ **Directions**

Write the base word for each of the following words.

8. started _____     9. opening _____

10. lifts _____     11. makes _____

12. washed _____     13. dreamed _____

14. worked _____     15. burns _____

16. spelling _____     17. stacked _____

18. caps _____     19. looking _____

20. dressed _____     21. hats _____

22. runs _____     23. reading _____

Name _____

© MCP All Rights Reserved.

## ▶ Directions

Read each sentence. Add the suffix **ful,
less, ly,** or **ness** to the word below the line.
Write the new word on the line. Read the
sentence again to be sure it makes sense.

**Definition** A **suffix** is a word
part that is added at the end of a
base word to change the base word's
meaning or the way it is used.

hope + **ful** = hope**ful**
slow + **ly** = slow**ly**
help + **less** = help**less**
sick + **ness** = sick**ness**

1. Jan was sick, and food seemed _____ to her.
   (taste)

2. It was _____ for Jan to swallow.
   (pain)

3. "Your face is pale and looks _____ ," said Mother.
   (color)

4. "I hope the doctor comes _____ ."
   (quick)

5. Jan's _____ turned out to be mumps.
   (ill)

6. "It's not too serious," the doctor said _____ .
   (kind)

7. "You must be _____ to get plenty of rest."
   (care)

8. "I don't like having mumps," Jan said _____ .
   (sad)

9. "Take a _____ of medicine," said Mother.
   (spoon)

10. "Then I will _____ read to you."
    (glad)

> **Directions**

Read each word. Make new words by adding the suffixes. Write the new words in the correct columns.

|  | er | est | ly | ness |
|---|---|---|---|---|
| 1. sick | | | | |
| 2. neat | | | | |
| 3. loud | | | | |
| 4. quick | | | | |
| 5. bright | | | | |

|  | ful | less |
|---|---|---|
| 6. care | | |
| 7. thank | | |
| 8. pain | | |
| 9. hope | | |
| 10. help | | |

> **Directions**

Write the base word for each of the words below.

11. kindness _____

13. smaller _____

15. coldest _____

17. useful _____

19. homeless _____

12. gladly _____

14. harmless _____

16. spoonful _____

18. sadness _____

20. taller _____

Name _____

▶ **Directions**

Read each sentence. Add **er** or **est** to each word below the line. Write the new word on the line.

**Rule** The suffix **er** may be used to compare two things. The suffix **est** may be used to compare more than two things.

1. Lisa is _____ than
   (tall)
   her sister Nancy.

2. Nancy is _____
   (old)
   than Lisa.

3. Their little sister Joy is

   the _____ sister.
   (young)

4. Joy is also the _____.
   (short)

5. "Lisa may be tall," says Joy, "but I'm

   _____ than she is."
   (smart)

tall  taller  tallest

▶ **Directions**

Add the suffix **er** to each word. Write the new word on the line.

**Rule** The suffix **er** sometimes means *a person who*. A teacher is a person who teaches.

6. teach _____    7. perform _____

8. sing _____    9. play _____

10. work _____    11. report _____

12. farm _____    13. print _____

© MCP All Rights Reserved.

## ▶ Directions

Read each sentence.  Fill in the circle beside the suffix that can be added to the word below the line to complete the sentence.  Write the new word on the line.

1. A puppy _____ Ann home.          ○ er    ○ ed
   (follow)

2. It was _____ to stay close to her.          ○ ness    ○ ful
   (care)

3. One ear was _____ than the other.          ○ er    ○ est
   (long)

4. It had the _____ legs Ann had ever seen.          ○ ful    ○ est
   (short)

5. Had it been _____ in the woods?          ○ ing    ○ ful
   (stay)

6. The puppy looked at Ann _____ .          ○ ness    ○ ly
   (sad)

7. It was the _____ pup she'd ever seen.          ○ s    ○ est
   (sweet)

8. "You must be _____," she said.          ○ ness    ○ less
   (home)

9. "We'll try _____ it," said Mom.          ○ ly    ○ ing
   (keep)

10. "I hope no one _____ for it," said Ann.          ○ s    ○ ing
    (call)

11. The puppy wagged its tail with _____ .          ○ ness    ○ less
    (glad)

12. Then it _____ Ann's face.          ○ ing    ○ ed
    (lick)

Name _____

© MCP All Rights Reserved.

▶ **Directions**

Circle each word that ends in a single consonant. Then add the suffixes to make new words.

**Rule** When a word with a short vowel ends in a single consonant, usually double the consonant before adding a suffix that begins with a vowel.

| pet | pet**ted** | pet**ting** |
| thin | thin**ner** | thin**nest** |

**ed**                    **ing**

1. tag _____ _____

2. rip _____ _____

3. jump _____ _____

4. nap _____ _____

**er**                    **est**

5. big _____ _____

6. fat _____ _____

7. cold _____ _____

8. hot _____ _____

▶ **Directions**

Circle the word with a suffix in each sentence. Write its base word on the line.

9. Today was the hottest day of the summer. _____

10. Joe slept longer than he did yesterday. _____

11. A bee skipped onto Joe's nose. _____

12. He let out a snore and sent it hopping. _____

Complete each sentence by adding the correct suffix to the word in parentheses. Write the word on the line.

1. Ed was tired of _____ on the bench. (sit)

2. He _____ the coach to let him play. (beg)

3. "I'm _____ you in the game," said the coach. (put)

4. On the first try, Ed _____ the ball. (fan)

5. Then he _____ the ball past the pitcher. (bat)

6. He began _____ and reached home plate. (run)

7. "Ed's our _____ player!" said the coach. (hot)

8. Ed was proud to be a _____. (win)

**Directions**

Write the base word for each of the following words.

9. shopper _____  10. swimmer _____

11. tagged _____  12. stopper _____

13. tipping _____  14. petted _____

15. dripping _____  16. rubbed _____

17. chopper _____  18. tapped _____

19. cutting _____  20. bigger _____

21. quitting _____  22. hopping _____

23. hitting _____  24. biggest _____

Name _____

© MCP All Rights Reserved.

▶ **Directions**

Look at each picture. Then make a word to describe the picture by putting together the base word and the suffix. Write the new word on the line. Be sure to make the spelling change.

**Rule** When a word ends in silent **e,** drop the **e** before adding a suffix that begins with a vowel.

| take | tak**ing** |
| large | larg**est** |

1. rake + ing

_____

2. hide + ing

_____

3. slice + ed

_____

4. shine + ing

_____

5. cute + est

_____

6. wave + ing

_____

7. write + er

_____

8. taste + ed

_____

9. smile + ing

_____

10. exercise + s

_____

11. bake + ed

_____

12. examine + ed

_____

▶ **Directions**

Make new words by adding the suffixes shown below. Write the new words in the correct columns.

**Rule** When a word ends in silent **e**, drop the **e** before adding **es, ed, ing, er,** or **est.**

hope          hop**ing**
large         larg**est**

| | es | ed | ing |
|---|---|---|---|
| **1.** use | _____ | _____ | _____ |
| **2.** place | _____ | _____ | _____ |
| **3.** smile | _____ | _____ | _____ |
| **4.** skate | _____ | _____ | _____ |
| **5.** glaze | _____ | _____ | _____ |
| **6.** rake | _____ | _____ | _____ |

| | er | est |
|---|---|---|
| **7.** fine | _____ | _____ |
| **8.** ripe | _____ | _____ |
| **9.** cute | _____ | _____ |
| **10.** pure | _____ | _____ |
| **11.** tame | _____ | _____ |
| **12.** nice | _____ | _____ |

Name _____

► **Directions**

Write the base word for each word below.

1. taking _____    2. hiding _____

3. shining _____   4. chased _____

5. bravest _____   6. used _____

7. smiles _____    8. bakes _____

9. traced _____    10. hoping _____

11. safer _____    12. largest _____

► **Directions**

Read each sentence. Circle the word that has a suffix, and write its base word on the line.

13. Carl was shaking his bank. _____

14. "I need a larger baseball mitt," he said. _____

15. "I want the latest model." _____

16. Nothing rattled when he shook the bank. _____

17. He had spent almost all his money on
    ice skates. _____

18. "I only practiced on them once," he said. _____

19. "Mom told me the lake seldom freezes." _____

20. Carl thought baseball was the finest game. _____

21. He could have used the mitt all year. _____

22. "I should have been wiser," he said. _____

© MCP All Rights Reserved.

▶ **Directions**

Read each sentence. Complete the sentence by adding the correct suffix to the word in parentheses. Write the new word on the line.

1. Dan has a little brother _____ Tim.                          (name)

2. Dan usually _____ to baby-sit with Tim.                          (like)

3. One day Dan's parents _____ to go to a wedding.          (arrange)

4. Dan had planned to go ice _____ that day.                          (skate)

5. His parents _____ he'd baby-sit with Tim.                          (hope)

6. He hated _____ his plans.                          (change)

7. Then Mother had an idea that _____ the day.                          (save)

8. "How about _____ Tim with you?" she asked.                          (take)

9. Dan _____ that it was a good idea.                          (agree)

10. "Taking Tim is _____ than not going," said Dan.          (nice)

11. Tim was happy to be _____ along.                          (invite)

12. "You'll be the _____ kid on skates!" said Dan.                          (cute)

Name _____

 **Directions**

Add the suffix **y** to each word. Write the new words on the lines.

1. sleep _____

2. frost _____

3. rain _____

4. thirst _____

5. air _____

6. dust _____

7. crank _____

8. rock _____

 **Directions**

Read each sentence. Circle the word that correctly completes the sentence. Write the word on the line.

9. Tom got out his old _____ sled.

   rusty            thirsty

10. It was the first _____ day of winter.

    sleepy           snowy

11. It was so _____ Tom's hat flew off.

    lumpy           windy

12. It blew his _____ hair into his eyes.

    curly           cranky

13. Sledding would be _____ .

    airy            tricky

14. Tom pulled his sled up the _____ hill.

    bumpy           dreamy

15. His sled made a _____ sound.

    squeaky          frosty

16. It was a _____ ride down the hill.

    rainy           speedy

© MCP All Rights Reserved.

Read each word and write its base word on the line beside it.

1. washable _____
2. soften _____
3. harden _____
4. sinkable _____
5. darken _____
6. writable _____
7. frighten _____
8. breakable _____
9. brighten _____
10. likable _____
11. straighten _____
12. lovable _____

► **Directions**

Read each clue. Write the answer in the crossword puzzle.

**Across**
1. to make something soft
3. it can be broken
5. it can be washed
6. to make something hard
7. to make something dark

**Down**
1. it can be sunk
2. to make something bright
4. it is liked

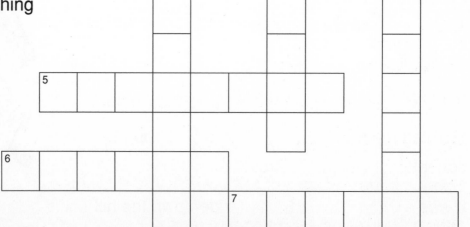

Name _____

▶ **Directions**

Circle each word that has the suffix shown in the box. Then write the base word on the line.

## Suffix **y**

1. It had not rained, so the playground was dusty. _____

2. The school children felt lucky to be outside. _____

3. The smooth soil was not too rocky to run races. _____

4. After playing, everyone felt hot and sticky. _____

5. Now the children wished it was cold and frosty. _____

## Suffix **en**

6. Natalie began to straighten the baby's bedroom. _____

7. The blanket she had washed to soften was folded. _____

8. She pulled down the shades to darken the room. _____

9. The very dark room might frighten a tiny baby. _____

10. She raised the shades to brighten the room again. _____

## Suffix **able**

11. Jack sorted clothes that were no longer wearable. _____

12. He placed the washable clothes in one pile. _____

13. Some clothes were suitable for his little brother. _____

14. Others would be usable for charities. _____

© MCP All Rights Reserved.

**Directions**

Read each word. Circle the suffix, and write the base word on the line.

**1.**

fastest _____

brushes _____

cupful _____

quickly _____

picked _____

kindness _____

brighter _____

trying _____

fearless _____

**2.**

darker _____

neatness _____

spoonful _____

tricky _____

washable _____

brighten _____

careless _____

wished _____

gladly _____

**3.**

darken _____

plates _____

friendly _____

rainy _____

slowest _____

player _____

restful _____

sticky _____

sleeping _____

**4.**

dancer _____

slipped _____

smiling _____

likable _____

whitest _____

begged _____

hiker _____

runner _____

finest _____

Name _____

▶ **Directions**

Divide each word into syllables. Write the syllables on the lines.

**Rule** A suffix that has a vowel sound forms a syllable by itself.

1. playing _____

2. lighten _____

3. spoonful _____

4. gladly _____

5. needed _____

6. playful _____

7. cheerful _____

8. lovely _____

9. shining _____

10. loudest _____

11. useless _____

12. darkness _____

13. training _____

14. eating _____

15. homeless _____

16. blooming _____

17. careful _____

18. laughing _____

19. patches _____

20. painted _____

21. wiper _____

22. snowy _____

23. hopeful _____

24. neatness _____

25. slowly _____

26. waiting _____

27. careless _____

28. rainy _____

29. brighten _____

30. useful _____

© MCP All Rights Reserved.

Read each sentence. Circle the word that correctly completes the sentence. Write the word on the line.

1. Sue hurt herself _____ when she fell.  gladly    badly

2. She had not been _____ going down
   the stairs.                                    useful    careful

3. Sue felt _____ with her arm in a cast.  useless    fearless

4. The pain kept her from _____ .   drying    laughing

5. A visit from Tony made Sue feel _____ .  awful    playful

6. It was nice to see a _____ face.  friendly    sadly

7. Sue thought his flowers were _____ .  lovely    carefully

8. The white daisies helped _____
   the room.                                    brighten    frighten

9. Tony also brought some ripe _____ .  wishes    peaches

10. A smile _____ started to cross her face.  badly    slowly

11. "You are the _____ friend," Sue said.  greatest    fewest

12. "Your _____ has cheered me up."  neatness    kindness

**Directions**

Divide the words you wrote above into syllables. Write the syllables on the lines.

_____   _____   _____

_____   _____   _____

_____   _____   _____

_____   _____   _____

Name _____

▶ **Directions**

In each box match the base word in the first column with a suffix in the
second column to make a new word.  Write the word on the line.

**1.**

| luck | able | _____ |
| cold | y | _____ |
| wash | ful | _____ |
| hope | est | _____ |

**2.**

| fly | less | _____ |
| loud | ing | _____ |
| peach | est | _____ |
| meat | es | _____ |

**3.**

| safe | y | _____ |
| church | ing | _____ |
| health | ly | _____ |
| say | es | _____ |

**4.**

| teach | less | _____ |
| home | ed | _____ |
| land | ful | _____ |
| cup | er | _____ |

**5.**

| sink | y | _____ |
| rest | ed | _____ |
| cloud | en | _____ |
| fright | able | _____ |

**6.**

| sleep | ful | _____ |
| light | able | _____ |
| spoon | y | _____ |
| clean | en | _____ |

**7.**

| ax | ly | _____ |
| sad | y | _____ |
| use | ful | _____ |
| rain | es | _____ |

**8.**

| fox | ed | _____ |
| hammer | ness | _____ |
| neat | able | _____ |
| stick | es | _____ |

© MCP All Rights Reserved.

1. knives _____
2. plays _____
3. shelves _____

4. boxes _____
5. churches _____
6. tagging _____

7. cleaned _____
8. parties _____
9. jumped _____

10. hopeful _____
11. thirsty _____
12. loving _____

13. loudly _____
14. chimneys _____
15. sleepy _____

16. painful _____
17. darken _____
18. sickness _____

19. receiving _____
20. foxes _____
21. hiking _____

22. wives _____
23. days _____
24. harmless _____

25. purest _____
26. glasses _____
27. leaves _____

28. shining _____
29. running _____
30. gladly _____

31. cherries _____
32. cooking _____
33. patches _____

34. begging _____
35. rolling _____
36. wolves _____

37. skated _____
38. weakest _____
39. snowy _____

40. straighten _____
41. homeless _____
42. smoothest _____

43. wiper _____
44. axes _____
45. picked _____

46. turkeys _____
47. whitest _____
48. sinkable _____

49. breakable _____
50. raking _____
51. daisies _____

Name _____

## The Book Sale

Mrs. Lopez's class asked to take a class trip, but they didn't have enough money.
"I've got an idea." said Lisa. "Let's have a book sale. We'll write books and sell them."

So they wrote, drew, and stapled as many books as they could. "We're ready on time," said Mrs. Lopez. "You've all worked very hard. You should be proud of yourselves."

1

— FOLD —

© MCP All Rights Reserved.

My dog Patches scratches and scratches.
He also catches a ball.
My dog Patches catches and scratches.
He always comes when I call.

Write a story of your own. Draw pictures about the story. Share your story with a friend.

4

Here are some of the books they sold,
and parts of the stories that they told.

**The Boat**
by Lisa Wong

I made a wooden boat
And it's not sinkable.
But if you stomp upon it,
That would be unthinkable.

— FOLD —

**My Big Brother**
by James Hines

I mustn't talk to people I don't know.
I shouldn't watch TV three hours in a row.
I wouldn't go play without telling my mother.
I can't wait to grow up like my big brother!
He is taller, smarter, and older than me.
Someday I'll catch up. Just wait and see!

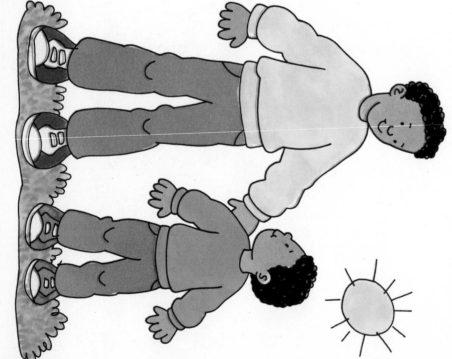

## 3

Lesson 52: Fold-up Book: Contractions, plurals, and suffixes

Name _____

▶ **Directions**

Find the word in the box that will complete the sentence. Write the word on the line.

**Rule** In a **vowel pair** two vowels come together to make one long vowel sound. When one syllable has a vowel pair, the first vowel stands for the long sound and the second vowel is silent.

| boat | tree | pie | crow |
|------|------|-----|------|
| leaf | train | tray | |

1. Joan will _____ Kay to paint walls today.

2. First she _____ Kay how to fix the cracks.

3. Kay practices on a _____ .

4. She _____ to fill the holes with plaster.

5. When the wet plaster _____ , the holes are all filled.

6. Next she _____ the holes with more plaster.

7. Then Kay is ready to _____ .

8. Joan shows her how to put on the first _____ of paint.

9. The clean brush _____ up the green paint.

10. Kay _____ that she has done the work well.

11. Joan _____ let Kay finish the job.

paint
coat
shows
board
teach
feels
dries
tries
seals
may
soaks

© MCP All Rights Reserved.

**1.**
seat
sail
soap
say

**2.**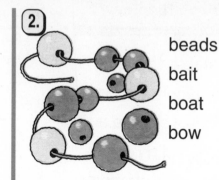
beads
bait
boat
bow

**3.**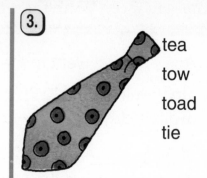
tea
tow
toad
tie

**4.**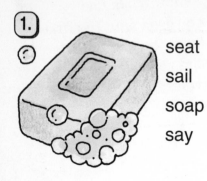
tree
tray
tried
toad

**5.**
clay
coat
cream
crow

**6.**
boat
bean
bee
bail

**7.**
boat
bait
beat
bowl

**8.**
made
meal
mail
may

**9.**
jeans
jay
jeep
jail

**10.**
seam
seat
snow
sail

**11.**
hail
hay
heat
heel

**12.**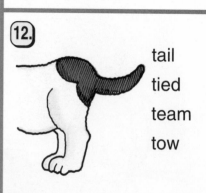
tail
tied
team
tow

Name  _____

▶ **Directions**

Underline each word with a vowel pair in the sentences. Write the words on the lines at the bottom of the page.

1. Ann and Ted went to the stable to feed the horses.
2. The horses liked to eat oats from the large pail.
3. Ann and Ted tried to ride at least once a week.
4. The plan for today was to go riding on the trail.
5. It was chilly, and the leaves were changing colors.
6. There were many pretty trees and bushes.
7. Ann and Ted stopped for lunch by a stream.
8. A toad jumped along the grassy bank.
9. The water flowed slowly over the huge rocks.
10. Ann put her feet into the cold water.
11. Ted lay on the grass and gazed at the sky.
12. A tiny boat with a red sail drifted by them.
13. Ann and Ted sat and dreamed.
14. Then it was three o'clock and time to go home.

_____    _____    _____

_____    _____    _____

_____    _____    _____

_____    _____    _____

_____    _____    _____

_____    _____    _____

© MCP All Rights Reserved.

**Directions**

Fill in the circle beside the word that will complete the sentence. Write the word on the line.

1. Jason and Jeff played in the _____ all day.      ○ snow      ○ soap

2. Making a snowman made them _____ very cold.      ○ foam      ○ feel

3. They went inside to play with Jeff's _____ .      ○ tree      ○ train

4. It felt good to remove their winter _____ .      ○ coats      ○ coal

5. Jeff's dog wagged his _____ to greet them.      ○ tie      ○ tail

6. Jeff made some hot apple cider for a _____ .      ○ treat      ○ tried

7. They had to _____ on the carpet to play.      ○ kneel      ○ know

8. A _____ on the train came off the track.      ○ when      ○ wheel

9. Jason _____ to help Jeff fix it.      ○ tray      ○ tried

10. Soon it was able to _____ along the rails.      ○ coast      ○ crow

11. The train ran smoothly the rest of the _____ .      ○ deal      ○ day

**Directions**

Read each clue. Then write the answer that contains the given vowel pair.

12. something to sail in              oa      _____

13. something we do to shoelaces      ie      _____

14. something that runs on tracks     ai      _____

15. something a rooster can do        ow      _____

16. something we do at recess         ay      _____

17. something that grows on a tree     ea      _____

Name _____

▶ **Directions**

Circle each word that has the vowel digraph **oo** or **ea**. Then write the words in the correct columns.

**Rule** In a **vowel digraph,** two vowels together can make a long or short sound, or have a special sound all their own. The vowel digraph **oo** stands for the vowel sound you hear in *book* and *pool*. The vowel digraph **ea** can stand for the short **e** sound you hear in *bread*.

1. Mike and Joe looked at the clock and saw that it was noon.

2. They stood up and left the classroom.

3. The weather was cool, so they grabbed their jackets.

4. They were ready to play a good game of football.

5. Mike threw the heavy ball, and it sailed over Joe's head.

6. The ball took a sudden turn toward the school wall.

7. Mike watched with dread as it went toward a window.

8. At the last minute, Joe scooped up the ball.

| **oo** as in **book** | **oo** as in **pool** | **ea** as in **bread** |
|---|---|---|
| _____ | _____ | _____ |
| _____ | _____ | _____ |
| _____ | _____ | _____ |
| _____ | _____ | _____ |
| _____ | _____ | _____ |

© MCP All Rights Reserved.

**Directions**

Find the word in the box that will complete the sentence. Write the word on the line.

**Rule** In most words **ea** has the long **e** sound as in *pea*. Sometimes, **ea** has the short **e** sound as in *head*.

| headlines | ready | heavy | weather | breakfast | bread |

1. Heather and Sid eat a large _____ every day.

2. They have _____ and jam with their milk and cereal.

3. Sid reads all the _____ in the newspaper first.

4. The _____ report said that it would snow later.

5. Heather and Sid put on their _____ coats and boots.

6. Now they were _____ for their long walk to school.

**Directions**

Find the word in the box that will complete the sentence. Write the word on the line.

**Rule** In some words **ei** has the long **a** sound you hear in *eight*.

| eighteen | weighs | veins | eight | neighbor | weight |

7. Lauren's health class grew from sixteen students to _____ .

8. Her _____ , Mrs. Parkhurst, is the health teacher.

9. She teaches that _____ carry blood to the heart.

10. Lauren learns how to read a scale to find her _____ .

11. It shows that Lauren _____ sixty pounds.

12. Lauren gained _____ pounds since last year.

Name _____

© MCP All Rights Reserved.

▶ **Directions**

Circle each word that has the vowel digraph **aw, au,** or **ei**. Then write the words in the correct columns below.

**Rule** The vowel digraphs **aw** and **au** have the sound you hear in *saw* and *caught*. The vowel digraph **ei** can have the long **a** sound you hear in *eight*.

1. Claud sat on the lawn under an oak tree and yawned.
2. Although it was August, he thought about a sleigh in the snow.
3. It would be awesome to see eight tiny reindeer.
4. He watched an ant crawl up a vein on a leaf.
5. He dreamed of being an author and drawing pictures.
6. The whistle of a distant freight train woke him from his dream.
7. He felt a bit naughty because his chores were not done.

| **aw** as in **saw** | **au** as in **auto** | **ei** as in **eight** |
|---|---|---|
| _____ | _____ | _____ |
| _____ | _____ | _____ |
| _____ | _____ | _____ |
| _____ | _____ | _____ |
| _____ | _____ | _____ |

**Directions**

Circle each word that has a vowel digraph. Then write the words in the correct columns.

1. In August Paul mowed the lawn at his uncle's big farm.
2. He liked to start in the morning when it was cool.
3. Sometimes he hauled bales of straw to the barn.
4. His uncle often helped him lift the heavy load.
5. During the hot afternoon, his head began to sweat.
6. He met his neighbors at the swimming pool.
7. Before diving, he looked for the deepest water.
8. By eight o'clock he was so tired that he began to yawn.
9. He went home to read a good book about weight lifting.

| **oo** as in **book** | **oo** as in **moon** | **ei** as in **sleigh** |
|---|---|---|
| | | |
| | | |
| | | |
| **ea** as in **thread** | **aw** as in **saw** | **au** as in **auto** |
| | | |
| | | |
| | | |

Name _____

| | | | |
|---|---|---|---|
| **1.** peach  bl _____ | **2.** hook <br> cr _____ | **3.** book  br _____ | **4.** rain <br> tr _____ |
| **5.** broom  bl _____ | **6.** eight  fr _____ | **7.** crow  sn _____ | **8.** hay  tr _____ |
| **9.** saw  str _____ | **10.** bread  thr _____ | **11.** goat  fl _____ | **12.** tree  thr _____ |
| **13.** beak  w _____ | **14.** pool <br> t _____ | **15.** break <br> st _____ | **16.** chair  f _____ |

© MCP All Rights Reserved.

▶ **Directions**

Underline each word in the sentences that contains a vowel pair or a vowel digraph. Write the words in the correct columns.

1. The rain and sleet beat on the windowpane.
2. It looked like the street was awfully icy.
3. A yellow school bus was caught in a ditch.
4. Neighbors told me I may have to stay home.
5. The headlines did not predict snow.
6. The weather wasn't even good for a sleigh ride.
7. I helped Paula bake raisin bread instead.
8. She showed me that it is easy to have fun.

| Vowel Pair | Vowel Digraph |
| --- | --- |
| | |
| | |
| | |
| | |
| | |
| | |
| | |
| | |

Name _____

▶ **Directions**

Find the word in the box that will complete the sentence. Write the word on the line.

**Definition** A **diphthong** consists of two vowels blended together to make one sound.

| oy = oi | | ow = ou | |
|---|---|---|---|
| b**oy** | b**oi**l | **ow**l | sc**ou**t |

**ew**
st**ew**

1. The Fourth-of-July picnic will be held

   in the _____ square.

2. The people will _____ together very early to plan it.

3. They will find a _____ of helpers.

4. A funny _____ will be there.

5. The children will _____ his magic tricks a lot.

6. Last year, he _____ pictures for children.

7. This year, he will make _____ disappear.

8. The cooks will _____ water for the hot dogs.

9. They will also make a pot of beef _____ .

10. Scouts will hand _____ small flags to everyone.

boil
crew
join
stew
enjoy
town
drew
out
clown
coins

© MCP All Rights Reserved.

Find the word in the box that will complete the sentence. Write the word on the line.

1. Sharon lives in the _____ across the street.

2. Her parents also have a baby _____ named Andrew.

3. Last night her family ate beef _____ for dinner.

4. Sharon is the one who _____ it the most.

5. Sharon's mother was pleased _____ everyone's appetite.

6. Andrew could _____ his food with his new teeth.

7. After dinner, everyone _____ in to wash the dishes.

8. Sharon dried them with a _____ .

9. Sharon's father wrapped the leftovers in _____ .

10. Andrew sat in his chair and played with a _____ .

| |
|---|
| enjoys |
| about |
| toy |
| boy |
| house |
| chew |
| foil |
| towel |
| stew |
| joined |

**Directions**

Underline the words in each row that have the same vowel sound as the first word in the row.

| 11. | toy | Roy | jaw | coil |
|---|---|---|---|---|
| 12. | loud | shout | moon | cow |
| 13. | owl | snow | drown | mouse |
| 14. | toil | yawn | boil | enjoy |

Name _____

▶ **Directions**

Circle the word that completes the sentence. Write the word on the line.

1. A team of scientists sailed to the _____ Pole.  South  Soil

2. They wanted to explore _____ places.  now  new

3. They asked a photographer to _____ them.  jewel  join

4. Everyone rejoiced when their goal _____ near.  drew  blow

5. They _____ they had succeeded.  know  knew

6. At first, the only _____ they heard was the wind.  screw  sound

7. They wore face masks when the wind _____ .  blow  blew

8. They fell _____ on the ice and snow.  dew  down

9. Sometimes they had to _____ to each other.  shout  show

10. They had to _____ snow to cook their food.  boil  boy

11. Often they ate canned _____ .  stew  slow

12. Everyone _____ tired and cold.  ground  grew

13. A chance to rest was cause for _____ .  joy  join

14. One day they heard a group of _____ seals.  noisy  choice

15. They saw a whale leap _____ of the water.  out  mouth

16. It blew air and water out of its _____ .  spoil  spout

17. The water looked like a _____ .  fountain  found

© MCP All Rights Reserved.

*Lesson 59: Reviewing diphthongs*

◆ **117**

Read each clue. Choose the word from the box that matches the clue, and write it on the line.

| coins | toys | stew | round | crowd | owl | flowers | house |
|-------|------|------|-------|-------|-----|---------|-------|
| boy | dew | mouse | cloud | bounce | mouth | crown | cow |

1. a form of money _____

2. drops of water on the grass at night _____

3. things that children like to play with _____

4. a place where people can live _____

5. the shape of a circle _____

6. a large number of people _____

7. what a ball can do _____

8. a headpiece for a king or queen _____

9. an animal from which we get milk _____

▶ **Directions**

Say the name of each picture. Choose the word from the box at the top of the page that names the picture, and write it on the line.

| 10.  | 11.  | 12.  |
|---|---|---|
| _____ | _____ | _____ |
| 13.  | 14.  | 15.  |
| _____ | _____ | _____ |

Name _____

▶ **Directions**

Say each word. On the first line, write the vowel digraph. On the second line, write the number of syllables in the word.

| auto | ____ ____ | cookies | ____ ____ |
| bread | ____ ____ | sleighing | ____ ____ |
| drawing | ____ ____ | taught | ____ ____ |
| reindeer | ____ ____ | because | ____ ____ |
| claw | ____ ____ | bloom | ____ ____ |
| neighbor | ____ ____ | vein | ____ ____ |
| awning | ____ ____ | eighty | ____ ____ |
| lawn | ____ ____ | noodle | ____ ____ |
| goose | ____ ____ | thread | ____ ____ |
| weigh | ____ ____ | bookcase | ____ ____ |
| jewelry | ____ ____ | breakfast | ____ ____ |
| shook | ____ ____ | sweater | ____ ____ |
| tool | ____ ____ | strawberry | ____ ____ |
| weather | ____ ____ | August | ____ ____ |
| headline | ____ ____ | daughter | ____ ____ |
| freight | ____ ____ | woodwork | ____ ____ |
| measure | ____ ____ | sleigh | ____ ____ |

© MCP All Rights Reserved.

Read each word. On the first line, write the number of vowels you see. Say each word. On the second line, write the number of vowel sounds you hear. On the third line write the number of syllables in the word.

| | Vowels You See | Vowel Sounds You Hear | Number of Syllables | | Vowels You See | Vowel Sounds You Hear | Number of Syllables |
|---|---|---|---|---|---|---|---|
| autumn | ___ | ___ | ___ | woodpile | ___ | ___ | ___ |
| shook | ___ | ___ | ___ | instead | ___ | ___ | ___ |
| bread | ___ | ___ | ___ | neighborly | ___ | ___ | ___ |
| weigh | ___ | ___ | ___ | naughty | ___ | ___ | ___ |
| broom | ___ | ___ | ___ | headline | ___ | ___ | ___ |
| sweater | ___ | ___ | ___ | shook | ___ | ___ | ___ |
| bookcase | ___ | ___ | ___ | pause | ___ | ___ | ___ |
| school | ___ | ___ | ___ | eighteen | ___ | ___ | ___ |
| reindeer | ___ | ___ | ___ | leather | ___ | ___ | ___ |
| spool | ___ | ___ | ___ | haunted | ___ | ___ | ___ |
| seize | ___ | ___ | ___ | receive | ___ | ___ | ___ |
| feather | ___ | ___ | ___ | claw | ___ | ___ | ___ |
| bedspread | ___ | ___ | ___ | drawing | ___ | ___ | ___ |
| weighted | ___ | ___ | ___ | measure | ___ | ___ | ___ |
| woodpecker | ___ | ___ | ___ | raccoon | ___ | ___ | ___ |
| laundry | ___ | ___ | ___ | jigsaw | ___ | ___ | ___ |

Lesson 60: Syllables in words containing vowel digraphs

Name _____

Say the name of the picture at the beginning of each row, and look at the letters circled in the picture name.  Circle the same pair of letters in each word in the row.  Then write the number of syllables in the word on the line.

| 1. | | gr(ew) | **1** | chewy | ___ |
| | stew | few | ___ | crew | ___ |
| | | jewelry | ___ | threw | ___ |

| 2. | | pointer | ___ | voice | ___ |
| | c(oi)n | broil | ___ | join | ___ |
| | | oilcan | ___ | spoiling | ___ |

| 3. | | boy | ___ | enjoy | ___ |
| | t(o)ys | annoy | ___ | Troy | ___ |
| | | royal | ___ | toy | ___ |

| 4. | | mouse | ___ | shouted | ___ |
| | sc(ou)t | bounce | ___ | cloudy | ___ |
| | | outside | ___ | house | ___ |

| 5. | | crown | ___ | now | ___ |
| | (ow)l | uptown | ___ | brown | ___ |
| | | frowns | ___ | flowerpot | ___ |

© MCP All Rights Reserved.

Read each question. Find the answer in the box, and write the word on the line.

| | | | | | |
|---|---|---|---|---|---|
| leaves | automobile | dollars | growl | draw | barking |
| clown | lunch | annoy | robin | glad | autumn |
| flowers | coins | connect | breakfast | hit | magician |
| join | painting | car | fall | woodpecker | joyful |

1. What two-syllable word names the season when leaves fall? _____

2. What three-syllable word names a bird? _____

3. What one-syllable word names someone who does funny tricks? _____

4. What two-syllable word tells how you feel when you are happy? _____

5. What two-syllable word names something that grows on plants? _____

6. What one-syllable word is a form of money? _____

7. What one-syllable word means "to put two things together"? _____

8. What two-syllable word names the first meal of the day? _____

9. What one-syllable word names something you do during art period? _____

10. What one-syllable word tells what dogs do when they are angry? _____

11. What four-syllable word is the name of something you ride in? _____

Name _____

## Is That a Seal or a Dolphin?

Have you ever looked at a sleek, swimming creature at a zoo, in a bay, or on TV and wondered what it was? Well, here are some ways you can tell what is what!

What you know about the skin and bodies of seals and dolphins will help you tell one from the other. Another way to tell them apart is by the way they breathe.

FOLD

© MCP All Rights Reserved.

If a seal puts on a show for you, it may walk on stage, bark with a loud voice, or dive for a treasure.

A dolphin does its show in the water. Dolphins can be taught to do tricks such as leaping high in the air and jumping through hoops.

Write a story about a seal or a dolphin. What tricks would you teach it?

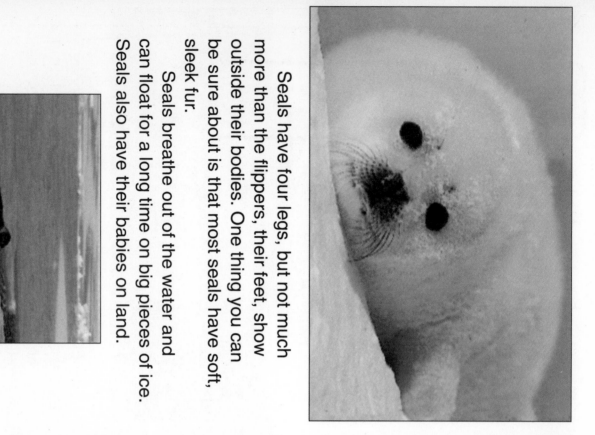

## 2

Seals have four legs, but not much more than the flippers, their feet, show outside their bodies. One thing you can be sure about is that most seals have soft, sleek fur.

Seals breathe out of the water and can float for a long time on big pieces of ice. Seals also have their babies on land.

FOLD

Dolphins have flippers only in front. Strong tail fins, or flukes, help them achieve good speeds when they swim. They have pointed, beak-like snouts. A dolphin's skin is smooth, rubbery, and hairless!

Dolphins need to breathe air often. They do this through blowholes on top of their heads. They live in the water and have their babies there.

## 3

Name _____

© MCP All Rights Reserved.

▶ **Directions**

Read each word and write its base word on the line.

**Definition** A **prefix** is a word part that is added at the beginning of a base word to change the base word's meaning or the way it is used.

**Dis**honest means **not honest.**
**Un**buckled means **not buckled.**
**Mis**placed means **not in the right place.**

1. displease _____

2. uncertain _____

3. disorder _____

4. misbehave _____

5. unfair _____

6. unhappy _____

7. dissatisfy _____

8. unfold _____

9. disagree _____

10. misfortune _____

11. mislay _____

12. unpleasant _____

13. disobey _____

14. unequal _____

15. discharge _____

16. uncover _____

17. misspell _____

18. discolor _____

19. disappear _____

20. unseen _____

21. misuse _____

22. mistake _____

23. untrue _____

24. disable _____

25. mistrust _____

26. uneven _____

27. dislike _____

28. unchain _____

1. unable _____
2. unpleasant _____
3. unhappy _____
4. unmade _____

5. disobey _____
6. misprint _____
7. dislike _____
8. displease _____

**Directions**

Read each sentence. Write a word from above that means the same as the underlined words in the sentence.

9. Messy bedrooms <u>do not please</u> Susan's mother. _____

10. Susan's bed was <u>not made</u> yesterday morning. _____

11. Susan was <u>not able</u> to clean her room before school. _____

12. Her mom was <u>not happy</u>, and asked Susan to clean it. _____

13. Susan would <u>not like</u> making her mother angry. _____

14. She cleaned the <u>not pleasant</u> mess. _____

15. Susan won't <u>not obey</u> her mother again. _____

Name _____

© MCP All Rights Reserved.

▶ **Directions**

Read each word and write its base word on the line.

**Rules** The prefix **re** usually means **do again.** The prefix **de** usually means **from.** The prefix **ex** usually means **out of** or **from.**
**Re**paint means **paint again.**
**De**part means **go away from.**
**Ex**port means **send out of.**

1. declaw _____

2. reread _____

3. defrost _____

4. exchange _____

5. express _____

6. rebuild _____

7. refill _____

8. derail _____

9. reopen _____

10. rewrite _____

11. retrace _____

12. redo _____

13. reload _____

14. depart _____

15. rewash _____

16. dethrone _____

17. exclaim _____

18. detour _____

19. decode _____

20. export _____

21. refile _____

22. deplane _____

23. redress _____

24. demerit _____

25. rewrap _____

26. reclaim _____

27. retie _____

28. decrease _____

1. disown _____
2. mistake _____
3. retell _____
4. exclaim _____
5. unable _____
6. reopen _____
7. dishonest _____
8. depart _____

▶ **Directions**

Fill in the circle beside the word that completes the sentence. Write the word on the line.

9. Al _____ Marie's invitation.
   - ○ reloaded
   - ○ reread
   - ○ refilled

10. He was _____ if he could go to the party.
    - ○ unsure
    - ○ unsaid
    - ○ unsafe

11. He _____ ice cream and cake.
    - ○ disagreed
    - ○ disowned
    - ○ disliked

12. He would go to the party, but he would _____ early.
    - ○ defend
    - ○ depart
    - ○ defrost

13. At the party Marie _____ her gifts.
    - ○ unchained
    - ○ unloaded
    - ○ unwrapped

14. She could hardly wait to _____ the bows.
    - ○ untie
    - ○ unpaid
    - ○ untrue

15. Al decided to _____ his stay for a few hours.
    - ○ explain
    - ○ exhale
    - ○ extend

Name _____

▶ **Directions**

Read the definitions carefully. Then read each word below, and write its prefix, its base word, and its suffix in the correct columns.

**Definitions**   A **base word** is a word to which a prefix or a suffix may be added to form a new word. A **prefix** is added at the beginning of a base word. A **suffix** is added at the end of a base word.

**re** + turn = **re**turn
quick + **ly** = quick**ly**

|  | prefix | base word | suffix |
|---|---|---|---|
| 1. rebuilding | | | |
| 2. recovered | | | |
| 3. unkindly | | | |
| 4. uncomfortable | | | |
| 5. unhappiness | | | |
| 6. discovers | | | |
| 7. misbehaving | | | |
| 8. displeasing | | | |
| 9. unpacking | | | |
| 10. exclaiming | | | |
| 11. derailed | | | |
| 12. repainting | | | |
| 13. reteaching | | | |
| 14. disagreeable | | | |
| 15. defrosting | | | |

© MCP All Rights Reserved.

**Directions**

Read each clue. Add the prefix **re, un,** or **dis** to the underlined word to make a new word that matches the clue. Write the new word on the line.

1. <u>painting</u> again _____

2. opposite of <u>locked</u> _____

3. not <u>returnable</u> _____

4. opposite of <u>pleased</u> _____

5. opposite of <u>kindly</u> _____

6. not <u>helpful</u> _____

7. not <u>washable</u> _____

8. <u>telling</u> again _____

9. not being <u>healthy</u> _____

10. not showing <u>honesty</u> _____

11. <u>reading</u> again _____

12. not <u>obedient</u> _____

**Directions**

Read each word. Circle the prefix and the suffix.

13. unthankful

14. disliked

15. unfriendly

16. redoing

17. unfairly

18. unpacked

19. exportable

20. distasteful

21. distrustful

22. detouring

23. rewriting

24. unhappiness

Name _____

▶ **Directions**

Divide each word into syllables.
Remember to use hyphens.

**Rule** Divide a word with a prefix or suffix between the prefix or suffix and the base word. Use a hyphen (-) to divide the word.

| | |
|---|---|
| redoing | re-do-ing |
| unfriendly | un-friend-ly |
| replanted | re-plant-ed |

1. rewrite _____

2. exchange _____

3. untie _____

4. dislike _____

5. unpaid _____

6. playing _____

7. spoonful _____

8. colder _____

9. softest _____

10. kindly _____

11. unsafely _____

12. repainted _____

13. distasteful _____

14. unhandy _____

15. mistrust _____

16. renew _____

17. displease _____

18. deplane _____

19. export _____

20. sleepless _____

21. boxes _____

22. dampness _____

23. rested _____

24. flying _____

25. unwisely _____

26. returning _____

27. unhealthy _____

28. retelling _____

29. unpacking _____

30. unkindly _____

© MCP All Rights Reserved.

**Rule** A suffix is a syllable if it contains a vowel sound. A prefix is always a syllable.
**read-ing   re-tell**

1. playing _____

2. loudest _____

3. disclose _____

4. softly _____

5. displease _____

6. harmless _____

7. spoonful _____

8. unkind _____

9. derail _____

10. dislike _____

11. rebuild _____

12. sweeten _____

13. unload _____

14. repaint _____

## Directions

Underline each word that has a prefix or a suffix. Write the word on the line, using hyphens to divide the word into syllables.

15. Vicky was careless with her gray coat. _____

16. She is unhappy because she lost it. _____

17. Now she needs a coat for the colder weather. _____

18. She is very uncomfortable in the cold wind. _____

19. Vicky's mom is displeased about the loss. _____

20. She tells Vicky to be more careful next time. _____

21. They will replace the lost coat on Monday. _____

22. Then Vicky will earn the money to repay Mom. _____

Name _____

© MCP All Rights Reserved.

▶ **Directions**

Study each rule about dividing words into syllables.

**Rule 1** A one-syllable word is never divided.
**coat**

**Rule 2** Divide a compound word between the words that make up the compound word.
**tree-top**

dog-house

▶ **Directions**

Divide each compound word into syllables. Remember to use hyphens.

1. into _____

2. doorman _____

3. birthday _____

4. cowboy _____

5. rainbow _____

6. inside _____

7. tiptoe _____

8. someone _____

9. sidewalk _____

10. sunshine _____

11. tonight _____

12. today _____

13. dishpan _____

14. highway _____

15. moonlight _____

16. bedtime _____

17. strawberry _____

18. headline _____

19. dustpan _____

20. hillside _____

21. sailboat _____

22. driveway _____

Read the story. Then write each underlined compound word below, dividing it into syllables.

## The Country Mouse and the City Mouse

"Welcome, dear cousin," said the Country Mouse to the City Mouse. "How kind of you to visit me."

"Well," said the City Mouse, "it's my birthday, and I wanted to spend it with you."

Upon hearing that, the Country Mouse ran into her tiny house in the ground. She soon returned with bowls of oatmeal.

"We can eat outdoors in the sunshine and fresh air," said the Country Mouse, "and listen to the songs of the bluebirds."

The Country Mouse ate heartily, but her guest just nibbled. Finally, the City Mouse spoke up. "I am used to a better breakfast than this. Let me show you what the good life is really like."

So the Country Mouse and her cousin set off for the city. At sunset they came to a big house with a doorman on duty.

"This is where I live," said the City Mouse, and they tiptoed upstairs to the dining room.

"Doesn't this look nice?" asked the City Mouse as she pointed to the pancakes, grapefruits, popcorn, and shiny teapots on the table.

Just as the Country Mouse was about to take her first bite, the door flew open. In came two barking bulldogs and a bloodhound.

The Country Mouse and her cousin ran for their lives and hid under a chair.

"Well," whispered the Country Mouse, "if this is city life, forget it! I would rather eat oatmeal in peace than a fancy meal in fear."

1. _____  2. _____  3. _____

4. _____  5. _____  6. _____

7. _____  8. _____  9. _____

10. _____  11. _____  12. _____

13. _____  14. _____  15. _____

16. _____  17. _____  18. _____

Name _____

▶ **Directions**

Study the rule. Then divide each word into syllables. Remember to use hyphens.

**Rule 3** When a word has a suffix with a vowel sound in it, divide the word between the base word and the suffix.
**kind-ness**

1. saying _____

2. sharpen _____

3. boxful _____

4. cheated _____

5. making _____

6. planted _____

7. hardness _____

8. homeless _____

9. needed _____

10. walking _____

11. newest _____

12. flying _____

13. cupful _____

14. kindly _____

15. playing _____

16. quicker _____

17. foxes _____

18. sleeping _____

19. safely _____

20. gases _____

21. fearless _____

22. smallest _____

23. reading _____

24. gladly _____

25. helpless _____

26. healthful _____

27. rested _____

28. careless _____

29. colder _____

30. loudest _____

31. neatly _____

32. faster _____

© MCP All Rights Reserved.

Divide the words into syllables, using hyphens.

1. painful _____
2. tallest _____
3. playful _____
4. scary _____
5. watching _____
6. sickness _____

7. smarter _____
8. darted _____
9. loudly _____
10. classes _____
11. interesting _____
12. singing _____

► **Directions**

Read each sentence. Choose a word from above to complete the sentence. Write it on the line.

13. Two _____ from our school visited the zoo.

14. We enjoyed _____ the animals.

15. One _____ monkey chased another.

16. The birds were _____ joyfully.

17. A lion roared _____ .

18. Otters _____ down a waterfall.

19. The alligator showed his _____ sharp teeth.

20. We learned many _____ facts.

21. The _____ animal is the giraffe.

22. The elephant is _____ than most animals.

Name _____

 **Directions**

Study the rule. Then write each word, dividing it into syllables.

**Rule 4** When a word has a prefix, divide the word between the prefix and the base word.
**de-claw**

1. unable _____

2. reread _____

3. distrust _____

4. recolor _____

5. depart _____

6. express _____

7. misprint _____

8. return _____

9. disown _____

10. untie _____

11. replace _____

12. exclaim _____

13. undress _____

14. deform _____

15. unkind _____

16. display _____

17. unpin _____

18. misfit _____

19. exchange _____

20. unfair _____

21. depress _____

22. displease _____

23. detour _____

24. unscrew _____

25. derail _____

26. renew _____

27. export _____

28. repaint _____

29. discharge _____

30. unfold _____

31. review _____

32. defrost _____

© MCP All Rights Reserved.

1. unsafe _____
2. discomfort _____
3. repair _____
4. refund _____
5. remove _____
6. delay _____
7. depart _____
8. request _____
9. displease _____
10. unlock _____

▶ **Directions**
Read each sentence. Choose a word from above to complete the sentence. Write it on the line.

11. Beth used a key to _____ the car.

12. She had to _____ her suitcase from the trunk.

13. She felt some _____ because of her heavy bag.

14. Beth had to _____ someone's help.

15. Her plane was to _____ soon for Boston.

16. There was a _____ in the flight.

17. The plane was _____ to travel in.

18. The mechanics could not _____ it.

19. Beth got a _____ on her ticket.

20. It did not _____ Beth that she missed her trip.

Name _____

© MCP All Rights Reserved.

► **Directions**

Study the rule. Then write each word, dividing it into syllables.

**Rule 5** When two or more consonants come between two vowels in a word, the word is usually divided between the first two consonants.
**hun-gry**

1. picture _____
2. pencil _____
3. confess _____
4. goblin _____
5. forgave _____
6. basket _____
7. admire _____
8. princess _____
9. complete _____
10. mistake _____
11. candy _____
12. harbor _____
13. plenty _____
14. children _____
15. pilgrim _____

16. sudden _____
17. number _____
18. silver _____
19. Kansas _____
20. master _____
21. finger _____
22. invite _____
23. kidnap _____
24. doctor _____
25. riddle _____
26. almost _____
27. chapter _____
28. surprise _____
29. dictate _____
30. butter _____

Write each word, dividing it into syllables.

1. magnet _____     7. circus _____

2. sudden _____     8. confess _____

3. blanket _____     9. picnic _____

4. plenty _____     10. almost _____

5. invite _____     11. puppy _____

6. hungry _____     12. bottom _____

▶ **Directions**

Read each sentence. Choose a word from above to complete the sentence. Write it on the line.

13. Meg took a delicious _____ to the park.

14. She laid the food on a _____ .

15. She had _____ of food to eat.

16. There was a _____ tug on her shirt.

17. A _____ was pulling it.

18. Meg _____ fell over.

19. The puppy was very _____ , too.

20. Meg decided to _____ it to lunch.

Name _____

▶ **Directions**

Read the rules. Write each word, dividing it into syllables. Then write the number of the rule that you used to help you.

**Rules for Syllabication**

1. A one-syllable word is never divided.
2. Divide a compound word between the words that make up the compound word.
3. When a word has a suffix with a vowel sound in it, divide the word between the base word and the suffix.
4. When a word has a prefix, divide the word between the prefix and the base word.
5. When two or more consonants come between two vowels in a word, the word is usually divided between the first two consonants.

1. airplane _____ ____

2. surprise _____ ____

3. homeless _____ ____

4. balloon _____ ____

5. smallest _____ ____

6. monkey _____ ____

7. donkey _____ ____

8. helping _____ ____

9. outdoors _____ ____

10. sudden _____ ____

11. later _____ ____

12. refresh _____ ____

13. quickly _____ ____

14. hungry _____ ____

15. hardness _____ ____

16. displease _____ ____

17. slowly _____ ____

18. safe _____ ____

19. curtain _____ ____

20. harmful _____ ____

21. backyard _____ ____

22. churches _____ ____

23. railroad _____ ____

24. circus _____ ____

© MCP All Rights Reserved.

Read each sentence. Circle the word that will complete it. Write the correct word, dividing it into syllables on the line.

1. Joe and I like to _____ at pictures.

   look                    pilgrim                 tiptoe

2. We sit out in the _____.

   churches                backyard                displease

3. Joe turns the pages very _____.

   ballroom                harming                 slowly

4. Here is my sister's second birthday _____.

   bottom                  party                   walnut

5. It was fun to watch her _____ her presents.

   chimney                 unwrap                  homeless

6. There is my _____, Goofy.

   puppy                   shallow                 walnut

7. That's a _____ at the zoo.

   tiptoe                  monkey                  smallest

8. Let's take some more _____ soon!

   quickly                 hardness                pictures

Name _____

▶ **Directions**

Read the rule. Then write each word, dividing it into syllables.

**Rule 6** When a single consonant comes between two vowels in a word, the word is usually divided after the consonant if the first vowel is short.
**lem-on**

1. robin _____

2. cabin _____

3. figure _____

4. wagon _____

5. travel _____

6. palace _____

7. statue _____

8. finish _____

9. river _____

10. clever _____

11. magic _____

12. visit _____

13. shadow _____

14. model _____

15. dragon _____

▶ **Directions**

Write a sentence about the picture using as many of the above words as you can.

_____

_____

© MCP All Rights Reserved.

Write each word, dividing it into syllables.

1. cabin _____
2. palace _____
3. travel _____
4. ever _____
5. magic _____
6. river _____
7. visit _____
8. wagon _____
9. figure _____
10. dragon _____

▶ **Directions**

Read each sentence. Choose a word from above to complete the sentence. Write it on the line.

11. There once lived a large green _____.

12. He lived in a tiny log _____.

13. He liked to _____ to many places.

14. One day he rode away in his red _____.

15. When he got to a _____, he swam across.

16. He came to the royal _____.

17. "I think I shall _____ the king," he said.

18. "I'll do some _____ tricks for him."

19. The king could not _____ out how the tricks were done.

20. He wondered if the dragon would

_____ visit him again.

Name _____

 **Directions**

Study the rule. Then write each word, dividing it into syllables.

**Rule 7** When a single consonant comes between two vowels in a word, the word is usually divided before the consonant if the first vowel is long.

**ti-ny**

1. lilac _____

2. polar _____

3. spider _____

4. frozen _____

5. moment _____

6. lazy _____

7. pupil _____

8. lady _____

9. pirate _____

10. pilot _____

11. cozy _____

12. motel _____

13. David _____

14. music _____

15. tiger _____

16. broken _____

17. famous _____

18. paper _____

▶ **Directions**

Write a note to a friend using as many of the above words as you can.

_____

_____

_____

_____

© MCP All Rights Reserved.

Write each word, dividing it into syllables.

1. paper _____     2. frozen _____

3. lilac _____     4. cozy _____

5. music _____     6. policeman _____

7. spider _____     8. pony _____

9. sofa _____     10. lazy _____

► **Directions**

Read each sentence. Choose a word from above to complete the sentence. Write it on the line.

11. A _____ gave us directions to the park.

12. A band was playing _____.

13. First we went on the _____ rides.

14. Then we bought _____ ice cream.

15. We sat by a _____ bush to rest.

16. There we saw a _____ spinning a web.

17. When I got home, I lay down on the _____.

18. It was so warm and _____ that I fell asleep.

Name _____

 **Directions**

Study the rule. Read each word and circle the vowel that is sounded by itself. Then write each word, dividing it into syllables.

**Rule 8** When a vowel is sounded alone in a word, it forms a syllable by itself.
**pyr-a-mid**

1. m a g a z i n e _____     2. o p e n _____

3. u n i f o r m _____     4. d i s a g r e e _____

5. a h e a d _____     6. C a n a d a _____

7. u n i t _____     8. t e l e p h o n e _____

9. d i s o b e y _____     10. a l i v e _____

11. o c e a n _____     12. e l e c t r i c _____

13. a g a i n s t _____     14. d o c u m e n t _____

15. g a s o l i n e _____     16. M e x i c o _____

17. e t e r n a l _____     18. m o n u m e n t _____

19. o d o r _____     20. a g o _____

**Directions**

Write a postcard about a vacation using as many of the above words as you can.

_____

_____

_____

© MCP All Rights Reserved.

▶ **Directions**

Read each sentence. Choose a word from the box to complete the sentence. Write it on the line.

1. Tory's family went to _____ .

2. Every day they swam in the _____ .

3. The marketplace was _____ .

4. Many _____ were for sale.

5. Tory brought a _____ to read.

6. The family climbed a huge _____ .

7. It had been built a long time _____ .

8. A man in a _____ explained its history.

9. Tory ran down the steps _____ of her parents.

10. Then she wanted to run up the steps _____ !

| |
|---|
| pyramid |
| magazine |
| uniform |
| items |
| ahead |
| ocean |
| again |
| ago |
| open |
| Mexico |

▶ **Directions**

Write the words from above, dividing them into syllables.

11. _____

12. _____

13. _____

14. _____

15. _____

16. _____

17. _____

18. _____

19. _____

20. _____

Name _____

 **Directions**

Study the rule. Then write each word, dividing it into syllables.

**Rule 9** When two vowels come together in a word and are sounded separately, divide the word between the two vowels.
**flu-id**

1. giant _____
2. polio _____
3. rodeo _____
4. radiator _____
5. graduate _____
6. dial _____
7. usual _____
8. science _____
9. poem _____
10. radio _____

11. lion _____
12. diet _____
13. ruin _____
14. cruel _____
15. pioneer _____
16. poet _____
17. create _____
18. idea _____
19. gradual _____
20. oriole _____

**Directions**

Write two sentences using as many of the above words as you can.

_____

_____

_____

_____

© MCP All Rights Reserved.

1. radio _____

2. piano _____

3. diet _____

4. diaper _____

5. quiet _____

6. cruel _____

7. graduate _____

8. poem _____

9. lion _____

10. violin _____

11. violet _____

12. giant _____

13. guardian _____

14. create _____

15. rodeo _____

16. dandelion _____

17. Ohio _____

18. science _____

19. idea _____

20. denial _____

21. radiator _____

22. fluid _____

23. ruin _____

24. trial _____

25. theater _____

26. pioneer _____

27. hyena _____

28. period _____

29. realize _____

30. annual _____

Name _____

 **Directions**

Study the rule. Then write each word,
dividing it into syllables.

**Rule 10** When a word ends in **le**
preceded by a consonant, divide the
word before that consonant.
**nim-ble**

1. turtle _____

2. puzzle _____

3. gentle _____

4. whistle _____

5. eagle _____

6. maple _____

7. pebble _____

8. simple _____

9. thistle _____

10. circle _____

11. purple _____

12. bicycle _____

13. needle _____

14. riddle _____

15. people _____

16. rattle _____

17. scramble _____

18. cradle _____

19. dimple _____

20. sample _____

21. thimble _____

22. temple _____

23. tattle _____

24. middle _____

**Directions**

Write a short paragraph using as many of the above words as you can.

_____

_____

_____

© MCP All Rights Reserved.

▶ **Directions**

Read the story. Circle each word that contains **le** preceded by a consonant.
Then write each circled word below, dividing it into syllables.

### A Day at the Lake

One day, Mary and her dad rode their bicycles to a
small lake. They parked the bikes under a maple tree
and headed for the boat dock. A gentle breeze made
the water ripple.

"I'll show you how to handle a canoe," said Dad.
"It's simple. You'll be able to do it in no time."

The man at the dock untied a dark purple canoe
and held it against the dock. Mary and her dad stepped
squarely into the middle of the canoe so it wouldn't topple.

"You're very nimble," said Dad.

Mary's dad showed her how to use the paddle as a
rudder at the end of each stroke to keep the canoe
from going in a circle.

Then Mary tried it.

"You must have strong muscles," Dad said. "You are
really doing well."

Mary was proud. She had learned to manage a
canoe without any trouble.

1. _____    2. _____    3. _____

4. _____    5. _____    6. _____

7. _____    8. _____    9. _____

10. _____   11. _____   12. _____

13. _____   14. _____   15. _____

Name _____

▶ **Directions**

Read each rule.  Then put hyphens in the words to divide them into syllables.

1. A one-syllable word is never divided.

   b o a t          g o o d          k n e l t          s m e l l

2. Divide a compound word between the words that make up the compound word.

   p a n c a k e     s u n s e t     a i r p l a n e     b a s e b a l l

3. When a word has a suffix with a vowel sound in it, divide the word between the base word and the suffix.

   m e l t e d     s o f t n e s s     s e w i n g     h o m e l e s s

4. When a word has a prefix, divide the word between the prefix and the base word.

   e x c l a i m     d i s t r u s t     m i s l e a d     u n s o l d

5. When two or more consonants come between two vowels in a word, the word is usually divided between the first two consonants.

   h u n g r y     b e t t e r     s u f f e r     p i c t u r e

6. When a single consonant comes between two vowels in a word, the word is usually divided after the consonant if the first vowel is short.

   c l e v e r     l e m o n     r o b i n     t r a v e l

7. When a single consonant comes between two vowels in a word, the word is usually divided before the consonant if the first vowel is long.

   m u s i c     p o l a r     p a p e r     l o c a t e

8. When a vowel is sounded alone in a word, it forms a syllable by itself.

   d i s o b e y     a l i v e     m o n u m e n t     u n i f o r m

9. When two vowels come together in a word and are sounded separately, divide the word between the two vowels.

   r a d i o     d i e t     c r u e l     i d e a

10. When a word ends in **le** preceded by a consonant, divide the word before that consonant.

   t u r t l e     c a b l e     t h i s t l e     b i c y c l e

© MCP All Rights Reserved.

> **Directions**

Complete each sentence by using the three-syllable word from the group of words underneath. Divide the word into syllables as you write it on the line.

1. I was _____ about seeing the play.
   excited                happy               worried

2. It was a _____ about a king.
   surprise                musical               drama

3. It was _____ on radio.
   discussed                mentioned               advertised

4. Mom and I went _____.
   alone                together               apart

5. We went on a sunny _____.
   Friday                Monday               Saturday

6. The _____ was outdoors in a park.
   theater                show               movie

7. We sat _____ a huge tree.
   upon                underneath               above

8. The _____ led the orchestra.
   violinist                conductor               drummer

9. The actors _____ us.
   entertained                bored               amused

10. They went on an imaginary _____.
    trip                journey               adventure

11. _____, it began to storm.
    suddenly                quickly               fast

12. The _____ became soaking wet!
    performers                violinist               actors

Name _____

## Caroline's Shyness

JUMP-ROPE CONTEST TOMORROW

"No, Mr. Diaz, I don't want to be in the jump-rope contest," Caroline exclaimed unhappily to her teacher. "I am just untalented."

Caroline was new at school, and she was unable to overcome her shyness. "How can I be in a contest with strangers?" Caroline thought.

1

© MCP All Rights Reserved.

The next day Caroline decided to take her jump-rope to school. At recess she nervously asked Nicole and Tiffany to jump rope with her. They smiled happily.

"Caroline, you are remarkably good," said Nicole. "I am going to redo our act to include you."

Write an ending for the story. Do you think they will do well in the jump-rope contest?

4

## 2

Nicole and Tiffany had the best act. They jumped quickly while chanting jump-rope rhymes.

Caroline knew she was a good jumper, too. She wished she were braver so that she could join them. Maybe they would ask her to be part of their team once they discovered how well she jumped.

**FOLD**

Caroline and her mother unpacked more dishes in their new home. "Thanks for being so helpful," her mother said. "You look so discouraged. What's wrong?"

"Oh, it's unfair, Mom," Caroline answered. "I hate being new. I'm uncomfortable around the other kids. They don't mean to be unkind, but I'm so shy."

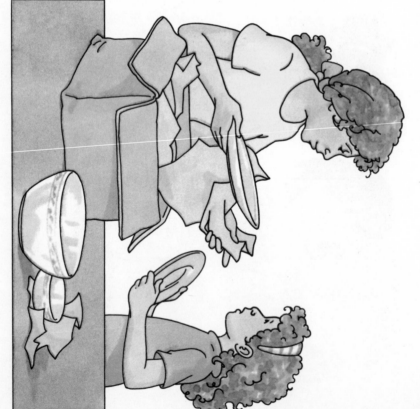

Name _____

© MCP All Rights Reserved.

▶ **Directions**

Read each sentence. Then rewrite it, replacing the underlined word with a synonym from the box.

**Definition** **Synonyms** are words that have the same or almost the same meaning.
**big—large**    **fall—drop**

| | | | | |
|---|---|---|---|---|
| forgets | closes | radio | tale | teaches |
| discovers | silent | loud | pretty | unhappy |
| woods | field | upset | glad | happens |

**1.** My dad enjoys reading me a <u>story</u> before bedtime. _____

_____

**2.** I am <u>happy</u> when we spend time together. _____

_____

**3.** He begins to read when I am <u>quiet</u>. _____

_____

**4.** He always <u>finds</u> a new story to read. _____

_____

**5.** This story is about a girl who lives in the <u>forest</u>. _____

_____

**6.** She wears a <u>beautiful</u> red cape. _____

_____

**7.** I can't wait to find out what <u>occurs</u>. _____

_____

Read each riddle. Write a word from the box to answer the riddle.

| woods | big | funny | hear | boat | close | beautiful |

1. I have four letters. I mean the same as <u>listen</u>.     I am _____.

2. I have five letters. I mean the same as <u>comical</u>.     I am _____.

3. I have four letters. I mean the same as <u>ship</u>.     I am _____.

4. I have five letters. I mean the same as <u>near</u>.     I am _____.

5. I have three letters. I mean the same as <u>large</u>.     I am _____.

6. I have five letters. I mean the same as <u>forest</u>.     I am _____.

7. I have nine letters. I mean the same as <u>pretty</u>.     I am _____.

**Directions**

For each group of words, draw a line from the word in the first column to its synonym in the second column.

**8.**

| fix | hurt |
| injure | gift |
| present | repair |
| raise | remain |
| stay | lift |

**9.**

| huge | said |
| pretty | large |
| told | quiet |
| silent | glad |
| happy | beautiful |

**10.**

| say | drop |
| fall | little |
| glisten | even |
| level | tell |
| small | sparkle |

**11.**

| fearful | crawl |
| reap | sad |
| creep | afraid |
| big | gather |
| unhappy | large |

**12.**

| handsome | attractive |
| swift | dreary |
| gloomy | marvelous |
| wonderful | informed |
| reported | speedy |

**13.**

| powerful | trip |
| strike | piece |
| journey | strong |
| store | hit |
| part | shop |

Name _____

© MCP All Rights Reserved.

▶ **Directions**

For each group of words, draw a line from the word in the first column to its antonym in the second column.

**Definition** Antonyms are words that are opposite or almost opposite in meaning.
**lost—found**

**1.**
| strong | dark |
| hot | cold |
| many | few |
| light | weak |

**2.**
| light | tight |
| loose | warm |
| cool | heavy |
| fat | thin |

**3.**
| large | fearful |
| sharp | dull |
| sick | healthy |
| fearless | small |

**4.**
| asleep | fast |
| slow | awake |
| friend | enemy |
| full | empty |

**5.**
| swiftly | quiet |
| noisy | slowly |
| difficult | go |
| come | easy |

**6.**
| hard | under |
| young | soft |
| descend | old |
| over | climb |

▶ **Directions**

Read each sentence. Look at the picture. Circle the antonym that will make each sentence tell about the picture. Write the new sentence on the line.

7. Danny and Fran ( climbed,   descended ) a hill.

_____

8. It was ( easy,   difficult ) to go up the steep hill.

_____

9. Along the path, they saw many ( dull,   sharp ) rocks.

_____

10. When they reached the top, they were ( happy,   sad ).

_____

Write an **S** on the line after each pair of words if they are synonyms; write an **A** if they are antonyms.

**1.**

short—long _____

sick—healthy _____

reap—gather _____

high—low _____

big—large _____

quick—swift _____

looked—searched _____

smoky—clear _____

above—below _____

**2.**

foolish—wise _____

woods—forest _____

friend—enemy _____

terrible—awful _____

hate—love _____

anybody—nobody _____

idea—plan _____

protect—guard _____

hot—cold _____

**3.**

shut—close _____

join—separate _____

quiet—still _____

inside—outside _____

narrow—wide _____

simple—easy _____

well—healthy _____

fast—slow _____

**4.**

rush—hurry _____

over—under _____

tall—short _____

display—show _____

lost—found _____

joy—sorrow _____

cool—warm _____

powerful—mighty _____

Name _____

▶ **Directions**

Read each sentence. Circle the word that completes the sentence and write it on the line.

**Definition** Homonyms are words that sound alike but have different spellings and meanings.

**right—write**

1. My soccer team ( beat,  beet ) every team this year. _____

2. We ( maid,  made ) it to the city finals. _____

3. We ( road,  rode ) to the big game in a bus. _____

4. We wore our new ( blew,  blue ) uniforms. _____

5. "Play ( fair,  fare )," said our coach. _____

6. Then he ( sent,  cent ) us out onto the field. _____

7. The time went ( buy,  by ) fast. _____

8. We ( eight,  ate ) oranges at half time. _____

9. We couldn't ( wait,  weight ) to continue the game. _____

10. The game lasted one ( our,  hour ). _____

11. Katie's goal ( won,  one ) the game for us. _____

12. The team's picture will ( bee,  be ) in the newspaper. _____

13. Our trophy will arrive next ( weak,  week ). _____

© MCP All Rights Reserved.

Read each sentence. Circle the word that completes the sentence. Write it on the line.

1. _____ have a favorite hobby.                    Eye        I

2. I like to _____ with my brother.               sail       sale

3. He _____ many things about boats.              nose       knows

4. He is teaching me to tie a square _____.       knot       not

5. Last week he _____ me practice.                maid       made

6. I still can't tie it the _____ way.            right      write

7. We sail _____ boat every weekend.              hour       our

8. We will sail today _____ tomorrow.             oar        or

9. We must _____ for the wind to blow.            weight     wait

▶ **Directions**

For each group of words, draw a line from the word in the first column to its homonym in the second column.

| 10. | | 11. | |
|---|---|---|---|
| break | knot | ate | wrap |
| not | stake | ring | wring |
| weight | wait | rap | eight |
| steak | brake | bare | bear |

| 12. | | 13. | |
|---|---|---|---|
| right | dye | I | pane |
| see | sea | led | sale |
| die | road | sail | eye |
| rode | write | pain | lead |

162   Lesson 81: Homonyms

Name _____

Read each word. Find its synonym in the box and write it on the line.

| tardy | trip | display | marvelous | large | chilly |
|-------|------|---------|-----------|-------|--------|
| smile | dull | repair | missing | hard | alike |

1. journey _____

2. big _____

3. wonderful _____

4. show _____

5. absent _____

6. grin _____

7. same _____

8. cool _____

9. boring _____

10. late _____

11. difficult _____

12. fix _____

▶ **Directions**

Read the sentences. Fill in the circle beside the word that completes each sentence. Write the word on the line.

13. Jack went to the state _____ .        ○ fare        ○ fair

14. He invited his best _____, Mark.        ○ enemy        ○ friend

15. The busy fairground was very _____ .        ○ noisy        ○ quiet

16. They _____ the roller coaster first.        ○ rode        ○ road

17. _____ people waited in the long line.        ○ Few        ○ Many

18. A man tried to guess Jack's _____ .        ○ wait        ○ weight

19. Mark tossed a _____ over a bottle.        ○ ring        ○ wring

20. They _____ candied apples.        ○ ate        ○ eight

21. _____ wanted to leave.        ○ Anybody        ○ Nobody

© MCP All Rights Reserved.

## Directions

Write a synonym for each word.

1. big _____
2. simple _____
3. shut _____
4. injure _____
5. swift _____
6. gift _____
7. small _____
8. lift _____
9. begin _____
10. ill _____
11. repair _____
12. tale _____

## Directions

Write an antonym for each word.

13. short _____
14. sick _____
15. hot _____
16. heavy _____
17. come _____
18. slow _____
19. soft _____
20. wet _____
21. early _____
22. weak _____

## Directions

Write a homonym for each word.

23. maid _____
24. beet _____
25. dear _____
26. our _____
27. bee _____
28. buy _____
29. here _____
30. fair _____
31. no _____
32. stare _____

Lesson 82: Test: Synonyms, antonyms, and homonyms

Name _____

▶ **Directions**

Read the hint. Then write each list of words in alphabetical order.

**Hint** Words in a dictionary are listed in alphabetical order. If the first letters of the words are the same, look at the second letter. If the first two letters are the same, look at the third letter.

**1.**

foxes _____

goat _____

beaver _____

camel _____

deer _____

antelope _____

elephant _____

**2.**

Danny _____

Ann _____

Frank _____

Carl _____

Betty _____

Ellen _____

Gerry _____

**3.**

bicycle _____

bat _____

bubbles _____

blocks _____

boat _____

break _____

**4.**

cheese _____

chop _____

chrome _____

chair _____

children _____

chuckle _____

© MCP All Rights Reserved.

Study the definition and the sample pages. Then look at each pair of guide words and the words below them. Circle the words in each list that you would find on a page with those guide words.

**Definition** **Guide words** appear at the top of each dictionary page. They tell you what the first and last words on the page are. All the words on the page are in alphabetical order between the guide words.

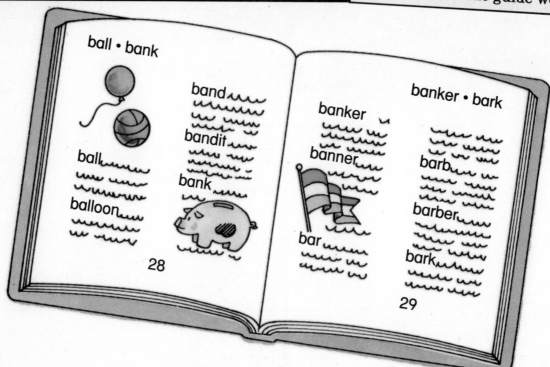

ball • bank

band
bandit
ball
bank
balloon

28

banker • bark

banker
banner
barb
barber
bar
bark

29

| 1. | **mice • mop** | 2. | **fish • gate** | 3. | **dance • day** |
|---|---|---|---|---|---|
| | mile | | five | | dark |
| | men | | frogs | | deer |
| | mitt | | girl | | doll |
| | moon | | gave | | date |
| | mask | | fun | | dawn |

| 4. | **rabbit • rake** | 5. | **wagon • wax** | 6. | **present • print** |
|---|---|---|---|---|---|
| | radio | | wallet | | pretzel |
| | raccoon | | wooden | | princess |
| | rocket | | watching | | propeller |
| | radish | | watermelon | | principal |
| | rain | | whale | | press |

Name _____

Look at each pair of guide words.  Write the word from the box that belongs between the guide words.

1. camel    _____    candy

2. dragon   _____    dressing

3. flat      _____    flute

4. jacket    _____    jay

5. ladder    _____    lazy

6. record    _____    red

7. think     _____    thorn

8. sailboat  _____    saw

9. whiskers  _____    wishbone

10. dazzle   _____    dear

11. zebra    _____    zigzag

12. rabbit   _____    raffle

jar
rectangle
flowers
candle
zero
deal
lantern
thirteen
race
drapes
window
sandwiches

 **Directions**

Look at each pair of guide words and the dictionary page number.  Write the page number on which you would find each word listed below.

| **each • elevator** 210 | **elf • escape** 215 | **fake • frown** 243 |
| --- | --- | --- |

13. elephant _____    14. favorite _____    15. erase _____

16. easel _____    17. English _____    18. farmer _____

19. family _____    20. educate _____    21. eggplant _____

© MCP All Rights Reserved.

Read each pair of guide words. Circle the four words in the box that would appear between those guide words. Then write the words you circled in alphabetical order on the lines.

**1.** can • cave

candy

case

cold

carton

cap

_____

_____

_____

_____

**2.** hide • hit

hen

hilly

hiker

hip

himself

_____

_____

_____

_____

**3.** sad • saw

same

soap

save

sand

sail

_____

_____

_____

_____

**4.** train • truck

treetop

trap

trot

tail

tray

_____

_____

_____

_____

Name _____

► **Directions**

Study the dictionary tips and the drawing. Then, decide in which section of the dictionary you will find the name of each animal. Use the drawing to help you. Write the number of the section in the box below each picture.

**Dictionary Tips**

Dictionary words are listed in alphabetical order, from A through Z.

If you remember the letters D, M, S, it's easier to find the correct page quickly in the dictionary. M is in the middle of the dictionary, D is halfway between the front cover and the middle, and S is halfway between the middle and the back cover.

1. bear

2. zebra

3. rooster

4. yak

5. camel

6. kitten

7. peacock

8. woodpecker

9. fox

© MCP All Rights Reserved.

**▶ Directions**

Read the information in each exercise. Then answer the questions. Use the drawing on page 169 to help you.

1. You are doing a report on prehistoric animals. Look up the word Tyrannosaurus.
   In which section of the dictionary would you find this word? _____

   You open the dictionary and see the guide words **unbroken • undergo.** Would Tyrannosaurus come **before, on,** or **after** a page with those guide words?

   _____

2. While reading a recipe, you see the word barbecue.
   In which section of the dictionary should you look for this word? _____

   You open the dictionary and see the guide words **by • category.**
   Would barbecue come **before, on,** or **after** a page with those guide words?

   _____

3. In a book of old Roman myths, you see the word Jupiter.
   In which section of the dictionary should you look to find this word? _____

   You open the dictionary and see the guide words **jump • justice.**
   Would Jupiter come **before, on,** or **after** a page with those guide words?

   _____

4. You want to know more about the continent. Look up North America.
   In which section of the dictionary would you find these words? _____

   You open the dictionary and see the guide words **music • nap.**
   Would North America come **before, on,** or **after** a page with those guide words?

   _____

Name _____

▶ **Directions**

Look at each picture. Read the dictionary entries next to it. In the box, write the number of the entry whose definition goes with the picture.

**Definition** Sometimes you will see two or more entry words in a dictionary that have different meanings but are spelled the same way. These words are called **homographs.**

1.

   **loaf**[1]   a portion of bread or cake baked in a definite form
   **loaf**[2]   to idle away time

   ☐

2.

   **bat-ter**[1]   to beat very hard
   **bat-ter**[2]   a thick mixture of flour, milk, or water, and eggs beaten together for use in cooking
   **bat-ter**[3]   a person who bats, in baseball or cricket

   ☐

3.

   **mole**[1]   a small spot on the skin, usually dark and slightly raised
   **mole**[2]   a small furry animal with poor eyesight that lives underground

   ☐

4.

   **scale**[1]   one of the thin, flat plates that cover the body of certain animals
   **scale**[2]   a device for weighing
   **scale**[3]   (in music) a series of tones either going up or going down

   ☐

© MCP All Rights Reserved.

Read each pair of dictionary entries and the sentence below them. Choose the entry whose definition fits the meaning of the underlined word. Write the entry number, **1** or **2**, in the box.

---

**1.** **prune**¹ a variety of plum that dries without spoiling

**prune**² to cut off or trim twigs or branches

Grandpa will <u>prune</u> the bushes in his garden. ☐

**2.** **fine**¹ very good

**fine**² money paid as a penalty for breaking a law

Meg did a <u>fine</u> job of painting the book shelves. ☐

---

**3.** **spoke**¹ a part of speech of **speak**

**spoke**² a bar coming out of the hub of a wheel

Danny had to repair two of the <u>spokes</u> on his bike. ☐

**4.** **bat**¹ a wooden club used to hit a ball, as in baseball or cricket

**bat**² a flying mammal, active at night

As they entered the cave, a <u>bat</u> flew out. ☐

---

**5.** **ring**¹ a circular band worn on the finger as an ornament

**ring**² to give forth a clear sound, as a doorbell or telephone bell

The bride and groom wore matching gold <u>rings</u>. ☐

**6.** **case**¹ the situation or condition, as in *a sad case*

**case**² a container

Janet put her new pin in her jewelry <u>case</u>. ☐

---

**7.** **post**¹ an upright piece of timber or metal

**post**² a position to which a person is assigned

Claude hammered the fence <u>post</u> into the ground. ☐

**8.** **mail**¹ letters or packages that are delivered by the post office

**mail**² armor made of metal rings linked together

Fran got <u>mail</u> from her pen pal in Australia. ☐

---

Name _____

## ► Directions

Complete each sentence using a contraction from the box. Then write the two words that the contraction stands for.

| didn't | haven't | I've | won't | here's | don't |
|--------|---------|------|-------|--------|-------|
| it's | we'll | isn't | we've | I'm | you'll |

1. _____ raining today.  _____

2. Jason and Lisa _____ be able to
play outside.  _____

3. "_____ got a new game," said Lisa.  _____

4. "_____ sure you will like it."  _____

5. "_____ have to show me how to play it,"
said Jason.  _____

6. "I _____ played it before."  _____

7. "Okay, _____ what to do," Lisa said.  _____

8. Later she asked, "_____ this game fun?"  _____

9. "Yes, but I _____ win last time,"
said Jason.  _____

10. "_____ have to play it together again."  _____

11. "_____ you want a snack?" asked Lisa.  _____

12. "After _____ played one more game
together," answered Jason.  _____

© MCP All Rights Reserved.

## ACROSS

1. a synonym for **noisiest**
6. an antonym for **cold**
8. a synonym for **everyone** or **everything**
9. a synonym for **look**
10. a synonym for **still**
12. tools for chopping wood
14. the beginning of a plant
15. a synonym for **vote**
16. a homonym for **pair**
18. spun wool or cotton
20. a homonym for **die**
22. the contraction for **I have**
23. a synonym for **bed**
24. a synonym for **hurry**
25. an antonym for **joys**
29. an antonym for **tough**

## DOWN

1. a synonym for **depart**
2. an antonym for **beautiful**
3. the opposite of **west**
4. a homonym for **their**
5. an antonym for **appear**
7. a synonym for **lateness**
11. a synonym for **each**
13. a homonym for **sea**
14. a synonym for **pigpen**
17. a synonym for **destroys**
19. short for **automobiles**
20. a homonym for **dear**
21. a sound reflected back

26. an antonym for **in**
27. a homonym for **wring**
28. a homonym for **weak**

Name _____

## Animals, Familiar and Strange

Animals come in all shapes and sizes. They can be tame or wild. They can live on land or in water. They can be gigantic or tiny. You'd need a magnifying glass to see the fairy fly. But you wouldn't use one to look at a Goliath beetle because it might be four inches long!

© MCP All Rights Reserved.

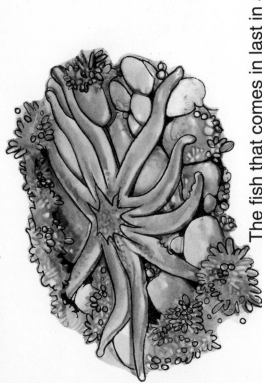

The fish that comes in last in a fish race is the one you may know most, the starfish. The one that comes in first is the one you may know least—the sailfish. It cuts through the water at 65 miles per hour.

What is your favorite animal? Write a description of it. Can you draw it, too?

4

Lesson 88: Fold-up Book: Synonyms, antonyms, homonyms, homographs, and contractions

## 2

You're probably taller than the shortest horse, a Shetland pony. They're less than three feet tall! But you'd look up at a thoroughbred. At nearly six feet, it is the tallest horse.

The lightest dog, the Chihuahua, could sit in your hand. It can weigh as little as one pound! The heaviest dog, the Saint Bernard, can weigh as much as 200 pounds.

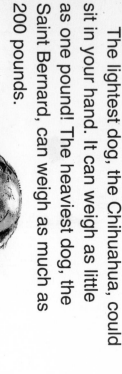

— FOLD —

A beautiful bird is the male bird of paradise. Male birds are more colorful than female birds. The plainest bird is the female brown wren.

The slowest creature on land may be the inchworm. It just inches along! The cheetah leaves it in the dust as this swift wildcat speeds by at 70 miles per hour.

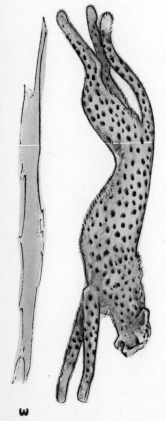

Lesson 88: Fold-up Book: Synonyms, antonyms, homonyms, homographs, and contractions